MW00850039

Our Time is Up

Our Time is Up

A Novel

by

Roberta Satow

International Psychoanalytic Books (IPBooks)
New York • http://www.IPBooks.net

Our Time is Up

Published by IPBooks, Queens, NY
Online at: www.IPBooks.net

Copyright © 2024 Roberta Satow

All rights reserved. This book may not be reproduced, transmitted, or stored, in whole or in part by any means, including graphic, electronic, or mechanical without the express permission of the author and/or publisher, except in the case of brief quotations embodied in critical articles and reviews.

FIRST EDITION

ISBN 978-1-956864-65-6

This is a book of memory of how I became who I am. Some of it is untrue by design, after all it is a novel, and part of it is untrue due to the prism of time.

Prologue

The weather in our house was stormy with the promise of thunder and lightning. I walked on the balls of my feet, as if to prepare for the thunderclaps that would slam me across the room. Before I started elementary school, I was alone with my mother when my father left for work at the Hunter Coal Company on Flatbush Avenue. As usual on Wednesdays, she put on her *shmata*, a sleeveless cotton housedress that tied across the front. The pink and green flowers on the dress accentuated the scowl on her face. She hated cleaning. But it was her life sentence. She filled a brown plastic bucket with hot water and added Ivory soap flakes and Jane Parker ammonia. Putting on her yellow plastic gloves to protect her nail polish, she dropped the wooden brush with stiff bristles into the bucket. Then she turned to me and said, "Go out on the porch so I can wash the floor."

She ushered me down the narrow hall with her gloved hand on the small of my back, and shut the door behind me. Once exiled, peering through the glass panes in the front door, I watched her on her hands and knees scrubbing the linoleum floor. Her breasts peeked out of her *shmata* with each forward movement of the brush, and an occasional smile crossed her face as she listened to Rayburn and Finch on the radio.

Outside, the trees tossed in the wind and clouds scudded across the sky. The porch shook from the elevated train that stopped half a block from our house on its way to Coney Island. At the foot of the concrete steps, there were three large dogs—a dirty German shepherd, a dark gray mutt with a wrinkled face and a black snout, and a long-haired white mongrel. They lived in an empty lot on McDonald Avenue around the corner from our house, and roamed the streets looking for food early each morning. Saliva dripped from the German shepherd's mouth as he bared his teeth and snarled.

I ran back to the front door. "Ma, Ma the dogs are out here! Let me in! Please, Ma!" I pleaded.

"Be quiet," she yelled, red-faced with sweat dripping, "and wait on the porch!"

I whimpered, "Mommy please, I'm scared of the dogs...."

The white mongrel growled. I pulled one of the rusted metal chairs as far from the stoop and the dogs as I could get it and crouched behind it. I watched the dogs at the bottom of the stairs jumping up on each other and barking loudly. They could run up the steps at any moment and I would be cornered. Then I imagined there was an invisible fence at the steps, but it only worked if I kept my eyes firmly fixed on the dogs. I stared at the dogs and chanted, "A hundred bottles of beer on the wall, a hundred bottles of beer, take one down and pass it around, ninety-nine bottles of beer...."

When my mother finished, she poured the brown sudsy water in the kitchen sink, rinsed the bucket and brush, carefully turned the brush upside down to air dry, untied her *shmata*, and turned on the faucet for her bath. I heard the water running. The dogs moved on down the block and the terror passed. I stood up and sat in the chair, breathing heavily and staring into space. She did not come out to get me when she was finished. She just took her bath and went to lie down on her bed. I could see her pull down the quilted bedspread as I stood on my tiptoes peering through her bedroom window that faced the porch. It was safe to go back in the house. The floor must already be dry, but I had to be quiet. I was crossing a mine field and had to hold my breath, tiptoe slowly, and not jostle anything. Opening and closing the door could cause an explosion. I smelled the light citrus of Jean Nate toilet water as I passed the steamy bathroom on the way to my room. I closed the door carefully behind me and exhaled.

PART I

MEETING JOAN

January 26, 1967

Sitting in the waiting room of the Washington Square Consultation Center trying to read *The New York Times*, I couldn't concentrate. I couldn't care less about Apollo 1 orbiting the earth; I was focused on a different kind of gravitational pull. I had been having anxiety attacks for months at Berkeley—dreams about being raped and episodes of terror with a rapid heartbeat during the day. To the utter amazement of my friends, I had taken extra credits in the last quarter to graduate early. I hoped that moving back to my parents' house in Brooklyn would make me feel safe. But I didn't confess that to anyone. And it did not work. I wanted to find a therapist as soon as I could.

It had taken over a month to set up an intake interview, be assigned a therapist and then set up an appointment. Now, finally, I greeted the receptionist and gave her a check for $25. She looked different than I had imagined on the phone. I expected a middle-aged Jewish woman with dyed blond hair—pretty but a little chubby. Instead, Barbara was a tall, thin redhead; she looked Irish.

I thought she had too much makeup on, but then again, I didn't wear *any* makeup at that time, not even lipstick. My brown hair was short and a little frizzy from the rain outside. I was 21 years old, but still wished an adult would hold my head to stop the throbbing.

It was Thursday morning at 9:50, so I imagined the people sitting in the waiting room didn't have regular jobs with set hours. No teachers, lawyers, or businessmen. There was a hall with doors adjoining the waiting room. I laughed to myself imagining a Marx brothers or Three Stooges comedy: doors opening and closing in random patterns with eccentric and wildly gesticulating characters exchanging places, all the while babbling incoherent phrases.

A woman emerged from one of the doors and called my name, "Rose." I smiled to myself. No last names because of confidentiality, I thought. The therapist beckoning me was about five foot one, just a little shorter than me. She was a pretty woman, not the kind that you turn around to look at, but her eyes radiated warmth. Her blue dress matched her sensible navy-blue heels. I thought she looked to be in her early thirties. When I walked toward her, she introduced herself at the door of the therapy room. "Hello, I'm Joan Wiseman."

I had imagined how her voice would sound. I didn't want a therapist exuding WASP elitism like Katherine Hepburn. I knew I'd never feel comfortable talking to someone who seemed so superior in social background—my Brooklyn accent would intensify and I'd feel like a *shlep*. A husky, sexy voice like Lauren Bacall, on other hand, would render me mute from envy. A high-pitched or nasal voice would evoke my contempt and I wouldn't be able to take her seriously. I sighed with relief when I heard Joan's voice. It was intelligent and engaging, but mellow and warm. The kind of voice you could snuggle up to.

"Please come in," Joan said. She stood next to a Danish modern desk with a black vinyl swivel chair that was turned to face a deep-seated chair across the small room. It was a chair you might find in a dorm room—a piece of coarse cloth hung on a curved metal base. It had no arms, and I imagined that when I sank into it, my behind was going to be inches from the floor. The room was designed to be innocuous, probably to encourage patients to experience it in any way they needed, but I felt humiliated by it. There were a few prints on the wall: Picas-

4

so's *The Old Guitarist*, a Miro abstract, and a farm with haystacks by van Gogh. They looked familiar; I'd seen prints just like them in dorm rooms. Pleased that I recognized them, I felt cultured. Joan was quiet.

Shifting around, I finally settled into the bottomless chair and folded my hands on my lap; my shoulders sagged.

"Well, I'm an only child and I grew up in Brooklyn. I just got back to New York after graduating from the University of California. Berkeley had the best political science department in the United States so I decided to major in that."

"Yes?" she beckoned me to continue.

"When I left Brooklyn to begin college, I got the cheapest ticket to San Francisco—a chartered propeller plane that had to refuel on the way. The flight took ten hours. I sat next to a girl named Maria who was returning from her junior year abroad in Florence on the same airplane, so she had been crunched up in her seat by the window for almost two days."

The part of me that wanted to entertain Joan gained steam. Joan was playing with her gold hoop earrings while she listened.

"She had pieces of a smelly tuna fish sandwich under her seat and a bent and tattered version of Dante's *Inferno* in Italian." The words came in a torrent. "She was lovely, but her body odor was overwhelming. I guess I got used to it. We had one of those intense conversations you only have with people you will never see again. By the time we were over Michigan, we knew each other intimately."

Joan's blue eyes reflected the light. The more intently she listened, the more I embellished the story.

"She told me about her boyfriend Johnny from Oakland, who was going to pick her up at the airport." My Brooklyn accent got thicker, my "r's" were dropping like flies and my voice kept rising. "I told her all about my mother and why I had to get away from her."

Joan sat with her legs crossed at the ankles. I noticed they were not the kind of ankles with protruding bones like I have. They were thicker; you could barely see the bones on the side. Joan switched from playing with her earrings to playing with a tussle of her hair as she listened.

"When the pilot announced we were landing in San Francisco in twenty minutes, Maria asked me if I was taking a cab to Berkeley. I told her I planned to walk over the Bay Bridge to Berkeley and stay at the Y. Can you imagine? She laughed and I felt really embarrassed. There was something stupid about walking over the bridge to Berkeley, but I didn't know what it was." I wondered if Joan knew how stupid it was to think of walking over the Bay Bridge. "From the map I just assumed the airport was near the bridge and I could walk over it. Isn't that incredible? It's over twenty miles from the airport to the campus. Luckily, she and Johnny took me to the co-op dorm."

Waiting for her to respond, I worried that she might think I was just babbling.

"Didn't your parents go over your plans with you?" Joan asked. There was something concealed in a fold in her voice. Her tone implied that my parents *should* have gone over the plans with me.

"No, my parents never asked about my plans." I sighed. "Once they decided to let me go they had no interest in my accommodations or the cost." I glanced at Joan to see if she was surprised, but she just looked concerned. "I had never seen a real palm tree," I continued, "only pictures of them on postcards my parents' friends sent while on vacation in Florida. And I had never seen a eucalyptus tree; I thought it was a type of cough drop. They're so weird-looking, strings of hanging bark and joints like armpits or crotches."

Joan smiled.

6

"When I got to the girls' co-operative dormitory, Stebbins Hall, I stood on the steps with my bag, having sent my trunk ahead of time, and knocked on the door. I had no idea it wasn't open yet for the fall semester!" I wanted to emphasize the strangeness of what I did. "Luckily, the housemother succumbed to my pleas and let me stay in one of the empty rooms. I had no place else to go." I pictured the white-haired housemother wearing a skirt and silk blouse although she was just spending the day in the co-op. "She had a bloodless elegance that Jews don't have." I rubbed my palms on my thighs. "When she gave me two sheets to make my bed, I asked her if it was one for each week." I hoped Joan would laugh, but she only smiled. "In Brooklyn we didn't sleep between two sheets. My mother had a duvet cover on the comforter and we used a fitted bottom sheet. The housemother informed me, in a loud voice, slowly enunciating as if I didn't understand English, 'One is the bottom sheet and one is the top sheet.'"

Now Joan was laughing. I liked the idea that she was trying to contain herself but couldn't help it.

I thought about the first time I saw my roommate Carole. She emerged from her brand new 1963 Volkswagen Beetle and dragged her matched luggage up the front steps. She wore tight black pants with stirrups under her feet to keep them securely in her black pant boots, and a stylish, low-cut sexy blouse. She walked into my room with the confident swagger of an Isadora Duncan without the scarf. I knew immediately that she was someone who knew the ways of the world that were unknown to me. Within a couple of hours of meeting her, I found out that both her parents had died before she finished high school and she had lived in an apartment with her sister Phyllis during high school. During those same years I was holed up in my room in Brooklyn with the kitchen phone cord stretched to the breaking point, talking to my friend Linda in a whisper so as not to be heard by my parents.

When Joan stopped laughing, we were both quiet for a minute. Then Joan said, "So you went far away to college, but you've come back."

"Yes." I bit my lip.

"Yes?" she prodded.

"I don't know what to tell you," I said. I took off my glasses and cleaned them with my shirt.

"Why don't you tell me what brought you here?" Joan asked, tilting her head slightly.

She was asking for a "presenting problem." I knew that because I had been planning this since I was 12 years old, and had recently re-read *The Fifty Minute Hour*.

Joan sat smiling, just enough to indicate interest, but not so much as to seem too eager. I noticed she had dimples.

"In my junior year my friends were all paired off with boyfriends and I felt lonely," I said, slouching in the bottomless chair.

"Yes?"

"I want to see you three times a week," I said.

Joan smiled again and I didn't know if the smile was pleasure at my request or skepticism about whether I knew what I was getting into. I took a deep breath.

"That's good," she said, pausing like a comma in a sentence, then continued, "but what brought you here, now?" Joan asked.

"My presenting problem," I said with a grin, "is that I'm the only college graduate who's still a virgin in the city of New York, or maybe the whole country."

Joan chuckled.

In college I had developed a habit of regaling Carole and the other girls in my suite with tales of Brooklyn. I had loved the laughs, but when it was over, I felt distant from my audience. I had come to

8

the clinic because I felt isolated and cut off from people, an observer watching myself interacting, one step removed from the experience. I called it my "Colgate shield." It was invisible and protected me from something, but I didn't know what.

Now, the hinges of my jaw tightened. "I started getting these terrible anxiety attacks in Berkeley."

"What were they like?" Joan asked.

I hadn't described the episodes to anyone before. My right eyelid twitched, and I heaved and sat silently for a moment.

"I was afraid of being alone," I whispered. I waited a few moments before continuing. "I kept imagining a rapist coming through the window. I didn't feel safe. Everyone thought it was crazy to want to come home to New York. I'd been telling them stories about my mother for years. I wanted to be in my parents' house. But now that I'm in a fellowship program at NYU, I'm living in an apartment on East 12th Street."

"Yes?"

"All my friends had boyfriends," I said. "Some are even married already." I thought of Carole and Paul. She met him when she started working at Pizza Hut soon after the beginning of our first semester. Paul was the manager. He was shorter than Carole and wore his brown hair slicked back like a muscular Sal Mineo. He wore tight T-shirts with the sleeves rolled up to show his bulging biceps and looked like a gang member with a cigarette balanced behind his ear, but he didn't smoke. Paul was pre-med and also a varsity wrestler. My impression of wrestling was from *Friday Night Wrestling* on television: two obese men dressed in some silly outfit with names like "Animal" or "The Chief" trying to cause each other as much pain as possible. I never thought of it as a sport until I met Paul.

"If all of your friends had boyfriends or were married, maybe you were afraid of having sex if you stayed in Berkeley," she said flatly.

My head jerked, I felt like a child caught picking her nose and wiping it under a piece of furniture. I stared at the floor.

"Are you saying… I wanted to be raped?" Eyes bulging, I tried to sit up in the cloth chair.

"No, I'm sure you don't *want* to be raped," Joan said softly.

My temples pounded.

"But rape means you didn't choose it," she leaned forward in her chair and continued, "you didn't want it. You're overpowered, so it's not your fault."

I covered my eyes.

"Coming home to live in your parents' apartment might have felt safe because you wouldn't have sex as long as you were living with them," she said.

"But now I have my own apartment…"

"So maybe that's what brought you here," she said.

"Yes," I said, nodding. "I think that's true."

"Unfortunately, our time is up for now, but why don't we set up our next appointment."

⟫⟫⟩⟨⟨⟨

I walked out of Joan's office in a daze. Walking home from the clinic, I thought about Carole. I remembered the regular reports from Adrienne about Carole and Paul's relationship. Adrienne worked at Pizza Hut with Carole and Paul. She was a Los Angeles Jew like Carole, but she was short and pudgy and, although she wore her long black hair in a flip, she seemed like a pre-pubescent boy. I thought about the first time Adrienne told me her suspicions about Paul.

"He's talking to 'Blondie' on the phone all the time," she said.

"Does Carole know?"

"No, they're not on the same shift. I think he leaves the shift and meets her while Carole's working her shift."

"Are you going to tell her?" I had asked.

"No, she's going to go ape-shit when she finds out."

"But that's why you need to tell her, " I said. "He's cheating on her. You have to tell her."

But Adrienne did not tell her. She didn't *need* to tell her. I did. It was like a stone in my shoe, I couldn't wait to get it out. I always said what was better left unsaid.

"If he cheats on you now, he will cheat on you later." I pleaded with her as we sat eating our salami and cheese subs at La Val's on Euclid Avenue. "How can you keep seeing him when he's still going out with Blondie on the side?"

"Her name is not Blondie," Carole said stiffly. "Stop calling her that. Her name is Jennifer."

"Who gives a shit what her name is—he's sleeping with her," I said, crossing my arms.

I had wanted to warn her. I was stepping over the line with my eyes wide open. I was jealous of her attention to him, but I was also genuinely concerned about her. I thought it was a matter of principle.

Increasingly, Carole felt there was nothing to talk to me about. The more questions I asked the more silent she became. I was confused. Asking questions was my way of expressing my interest in a person, but Carole experienced it as prying, intrusive and critical. And she was right. I could not understand how she could have sex with someone who was having sex with someone else. Since I was afraid of having sex with *anyone*, even if monogamous, it was incomprehensible to me.

"So, did you see Paul today?" I asked on one of the occasions she came back to our room to change her clothes.

"Yes, he was working lunch when I was there."

"Was Jennifer there too?"

"No, but she called him while we were both working," she said.

I waited for more. But she did not continue. I wanted to ask her myriad questions: Is he still seeing her? How can you stand it? But I contained myself. I just sat there in the awkward silence. She picked up her bag and walked toward the door.

"Oh, no, please don't do that. I'm sorry. I'm really sorry," I cried.

She walked out and slammed the door behind her.

Three months into the first semester, Carole told me she was moving out at the end of the semester and she was going to room with Adrienne.

Carole and Adrienne moved to a three-bedroom house on Parker Street on the south side of campus. It was on a tree-lined street and the house had a fireplace and a big eat-in kitchen. They invited another girl from the co-op, Laurie, to be the third roommate and I felt abandoned and devastated. Carole bought a queen-sized bed in expectation of an ongoing relationship with Paul. It was the kind of house a family could live in; they were living like adults. It was a half-hour walk from the co-op where I continued to live, but to me she had left the country.

The Yeshiva

The streets were littered with partly-eaten sandwiches, used tissues and empty bottles. Although I'd lived in Brooklyn until I was 18, I'd never been to Williamsburg. It was a neighborhood that I'd driven through in the back seat of my father's Ford, watching the men in black suits and large black hats and the young women in *sheitels*, wigs that Orthodox Jewish women wear after they are married, pushing baby carriages on the street. It was a place on the way to some other place; it was never a destination.

I needed a job to supplement my graduate fellowship in sociology at New York University to pay Joan $75 for my three sessions each week. I had been doing research for a professor sporadically, but I needed a steady income. I saw an ad for a part-time teaching job at a yeshiva in Brooklyn and thought it would be more lucrative than being a waitress. I knew tips would be lower if I waited tables at lunch rather than dinner, but night classes at New York University limited my shifts.

As I walked from the elevated train station, I could smell garbage and see stains on the walls left from men who couldn't contain themselves until they reached a restroom. I felt unsafe walking to *Bais Yaakov* for my interview on that late August afternoon. The people I passed spoke Spanish and sat on the steps outside their apartments talking and laughing. After a few blocks, the terrain changed—I started seeing men in black suits, dark untrimmed beards and black hats.

It was such an unlikely mix—Puerto Ricans and Hassidic Jews. But I knew I must be going in the right direction.

When I got to the building that matched the address I had written down, I thought perhaps I had made a mistake. It didn't appear to be a school because it was a brownstone, but there was a sign in front with Hebrew letters so I assumed I was at the right place. When I opened the door into the entry, the old radiator made hissing noises like a group of baseball fans when their favorite batter strikes out. It reminded me of our house on Webster Avenue; the radiators seeped heat even in the summer and the floors creaked. I felt sweat dripping down the side of my blouse. Thick yellow paint was peeling from the ceiling and the wooden bench in the hall was chipped from years of girls throwing heavy books and bags on it.

Two girls wearing skirts down to their ankles and blouses with long sleeves were excitedly speaking Yiddish. One of the girls, the taller one, asked if she could help me.

"Yes, thank you. I'm here to see Mrs. Goldstein."

"That's her office down the hall on the right," the tall girl said in heavily accented English.

Bais Yaakov was an ultra-Orthodox Jewish middle and high school for girls, and I had applied to teach eighth-grade English. The principal, Mrs. Goldstein, was a forty-ish woman who wore a *sheitel* and the kind of black shoes old women wear when their bunions can no longer fit into store-bought shoes.

"Good morning, you must be Rose," she said with a Yiddish accent similar to that of the girls I'd just met. I wondered if she was born in Eastern Europe and had somehow escaped the Holocaust. She ushered me to an old wooden chair next to her desk.

Her weather-beaten face made her look like life had blown her around. On the windowsill sat a bloomless orchid with roots that had grown well beyond the confines of the pot, and a cactus with brown edges.

"Yes, good morning," I said with a tepid smile.

"Tell me about yourself," Mrs. Goldstein said. Her veined hand rested on her chin as she awaited my response.

"Well, let's see. I grew up in Brooklyn. I'm twenty-two and graduated from the University of California. I'm in a graduate program in sociology at NYU."

"Great," she said. "You will be teaching a class of thirty girls. They have religious classes all morning and then they have English literature after lunch. So you will be teaching from one to two, Mondays through Thursdays. Is that agreeable to you?"

"Yes, sure. Is there a syllabus or a reading list?"

"No, this is a private school. There's no New York State Regents exam or anything of that sort. Just teach them how to write properly in English. That's all." She stood up and extended her hand. She did not ask for a transcript, a resume, or even a reference.

She hired me without asking if I majored in English in college. I wondered if I was the only applicant for the job. She did not care about my credentials. In fact, I had never taken even one English class in college. At Berkeley you had a choice of English I or Speech I, and I took Speech because it was a literature course—just not exclusively English authors. For example, we read the *Book of Job* and *Notes from the Underground*.

Walking back to the elevated train, I thought about my speech teacher at Cal—Virgil Grillo. About 25 years-old, he chain-smoked Marlboros and drank coffee from a styrofoam cup as he discussed readings with the class. He was from Brooklyn, and I fantasized that his parents owned Grillo's Fish Store on Newkirk Plaza. Somehow imagining that forged a special connection, that I knew his roots and he knew mine.

Sitting in the front row, right in front of his desk, I was mesmerized by the way his lips barely held onto the cigarette that hung from his mouth. I felt a contraction in my crotch when I looked at his muscular shoulders, the way his upper thighs bulged through his chinos, and the dark curly hairs on his lower calf that peeked out above his socks when he crossed his legs.

"So what did you think of Job?" he asked.

Up went my hand immediately, and he beamed in anticipation as I blurted out, "I think he was a *schmuck*." The other students were stone-faced, but he laughed so hard he almost fell off his perch on the desk.

Part of me had felt embarrassed and part of me enjoyed it. But it left me feeling like one of the unwashed masses. I made people laugh and that felt powerful, but I felt, in the end, they were laughing at my crass directness. I could have said, "I felt ambivalent about his faith in God. I would have lost my faith if I had suffered those losses." I could have said that. But I chose to say something that would announce to Mr. Grillo and the rest of the class, "I'm a New York Jew."

A week after the interview with Mrs. Goldstein, I arrived for my first class at *Bais Yaakov*. The girls in my class were bright and eager to know about the outside world. They were eager to find out about me.

A girl in the back of the classroom waved her hand back and forth to be recognized.

"Yes," I pointed to her. "What is your name?"

"Frume Minkowitz," she responded.

"Hello Frume, do you have a question?"

"Where are you from?" she asked with a smile.

"I'm from Brooklyn originally," I said. "But now I live in Manhattan."

16

The class started to chortle and poke each other.

"Why is that funny?" I asked.

Frume's eyes lit up and her brown eyes opened wide as she called out, "We're from Brooklyn too!"

They were all born in Brooklyn, probably at Maimonides Hospital just like me. They lived in Borough Park, not far from where I grew up. But Yiddish was their first language—they spoke it at home and with their friends. The girls explained that they did not watch television or go to the library or talk to boys who were not relatives. I decided to introduce them to the outside world, beginning with poetry. I mimeographed copies of T. S. Eliot's "The Hollow Men" at NYU and handed them out to the class. Then I read aloud:

> We are the hollow men
> We are the stuffed men
> Leaning together
> Headpiece filled with straw. Alas!
> Our dried voices, when
> We whisper together
> Are quiet and meaningless
> As wind in dry grass
> Or rats' feet over broken glass
> In our dry cellar.

Rifka Frankel sat in the front row and concentrated so hard on the poem that her brown eyes seemed never to blink.

"Who are the hollow men?" I asked.

Rifka brushed her chestnut hair to the side with her left hand and waved her right hand in the air enthusiastically so that I would not dare call on anyone else first.

"I think the hollow men are the people who live in the world outside of our community. They are hollow and stuffed. They have no meaning in their lives."

Impressed with Rifka's ability to see that Eliot was talking about the human condition in the modern world, I was also astonished that she didn't see her religious school and community as constricting. Rifka saw it as *protecting* her from hollowness.

"That's very insightful Rifka," I smiled and nodded with eyes wide. "Does anyone else have any ideas?"

Frume raised her hand. Frume wasn't as bright as Rifka, but she knew I was a saboteur and was excited by it. "Yes, Frume, what do you think?"

"I don't think T. S. Eliot would say that Judaism is an alternative to hollowness," she said. She looked directly into my eyes as if to say, "I know what you're getting at!"

I chuckled with delight, but then realized I'd better be careful not to offend the rest of the girls.

I wore long dresses with full-length sleeves to cover my elbows and knees, but Frume knew I was an outsider. I had left Berkeley only a few months before and brought my own version of the Free Speech Movement to *Bais Yaakov*. In addition to Eliot's poems, I assigned *The Scarlet Letter*. The girls were very excited about the material and there were always interesting discussions in class.

Frume always came up to my desk after class to talk about things going on in her life. One afternoon she stood near my desk and waited until the other girls left the room.

"You know my mother and father want to get a *shadchan* for me?"

"A what?"

"A *shadchan*. It's a matchmaker. They want to set up a marriage for me."

"But Frume, you're in the eighth grade."

"Well, in our community, that's when the match is made. Chava Mandelbaum has been engaged for a year already. He's the son of a friend of my uncle's wife."

"What does this mean for you?"

"It means I will marry Chaim Teitelbaum when I'm 17 years old."

"But what about going to college and majoring in English?"

"No, they won't let me go to college. None of us are allowed to go to college—they won't send transcripts to any colleges. It's forbidden for girls."

I felt short of breath. "Frume, you mean *none* of you are going to college? Rifka is not going to college?"

"That's right, none of us are going."

"I'm so sorry Frume, I didn't understand that."

The next week I brought my portable stereo to class and played the new Simon and Garfunkel single, "The Dangling Conversation."

Miriam Feigelbaum was the first to raise her hand. "That's amazing. I never heard anything like that before."

"What kind of music do you listen to at home?"

"Klezmer or cantor's music."

"What's klezmer?" I asked.

"It's Yiddish music," Rifka said. "It takes stories from the Bible and stuff and the words are in Yiddish."

"Do you ever watch television?"

"No, we don't," Frume said sadly, "we don't have a television."

After class Frume came up to my desk and waited for all the other girls to ask their questions and move on to their next class.

"My parents are really old-fashioned, they're pretty old," she said.

"How old are they?"

"Well, my father's 61 and my mother's 52. They got married late because they were both in camps and met after the war in a DP camp." Her manner was matter-of-fact, as if she were telling me what she'd brought for lunch that day. "My father lost his first wife and two children at Bergen-Belsen and my mother lost her parents and three sisters and a brother at Buchenwald. They were in the camp for two years because the British wouldn't let them go to Palestine. My father started a newspaper at the camp, *Unzer Shtimme.* Then the British finally let them go."

My head was throbbing—so much loss. How could they ever metabolize it? Finally I regained my composure.

"How did they get to Brooklyn?"

"They got to Israel after Independence in 1948 and just before the war with the Arabs, but after two years they decided to come to the United States."

"How come?"

"My father's brother was living in Brooklyn and tracked down my father in Israel and wanted him to come to Brooklyn and work in his printing business. My father didn't know my uncle had survived, so he was very happy."

Each day, after class, when no one else was around, Frume stopped at my desk to talk.

Monday: "You know my parents are old and they have suffered so much. It makes me wonder, How could God have let the Nazis kill six million Jews?"

"That's a tough question." I smiled in recognition; I had often asked myself the same question. I felt torn between pleasure that Frume was becoming an intellectual and sadness that her questioning was not just intellectual—much of her family had been murdered.

Tuesday: "My parents have suffered so much. I don't want to do anything to upset them."

"Yes, I can understand that, considering everything they've been through." But I didn't fully digest it because I still had the impulse to blurt out, "But just because they suffered, they can't make you do this."

Wednesday: "My parents want me to marry this boy I don't even know."

"Is that scary?" I asked, trying to sound like Joan.

Thursday: "You know, sometimes I'm not sure I believe in God."

"I can understand that," I said.

February 23, 1967

Arriving at the clinic ten minutes early, the same people I had seen for the prior three weeks sat in the waiting room, but they were not a group. They were solo travelers. A middle-aged woman wearing a tattered sweater was trying not to look at anyone; she kept her eyes on her book. When she was called by her therapist, she left the smell of mothballs behind her. She greeted her therapist, but it was unintelligible to me, like someone talking into her hand. A twenty-something young man focused on the Braque print on the wall, as if it was the first time he'd seen it. His head looked like a beer can thrust up from his collared shirt—with a thick neck and flat top. Although it was winter, he was wearing a cotton jacket. I imagined he might be a military man, while I thought the disheveled heavy-set woman reading Dostoevsky must be an NYU professor. She doesn't care how she looks, I thought to myself; her life is all in her head. The few female professors I had met in my first year of graduate school were all aging single women. Glad they did not go to the beauty parlor and spray their hair like my mother and her friends, I was also dismayed that they didn't wear makeup or color their hair when it started to get gray. I didn't want to end up that way either.

The first door on the left opened and a young woman in a suit carrying a Chanel bag and matching briefcase walked out. I decided she must be a lawyer. She had earnest blue-green eyes and the kind of Nordic blond hair I had only seen in its artificial form on women with dark roots. I imagined the Chanel lady was in therapy because she wasn't married and couldn't sustain a relationship. Chanel lady headed to the ladies' room; I assumed it was to fix her bleeding mascara.

Joan looked at me and smiled warmly. She was wearing a navy skirt that just touched her knee and a blouse the color of a tennis ball. I imagined the coordination was effortless, a natural ability to put things together that belonged.

"There's this guy in my criminology class who's really smart and attractive," I began after sinking into the bottomless chair, "but I feel I'm just never going to have a real relationship." I stopped, hoping Joan would respond.

"A *real* relationship?" Joan asked.

"Yeah, I've had relationships if you want to call them that. Short and nothing much." I shrugged.

"What were your first relationships like?" Her tone was soft and nuanced.

"I only had a few dates during college." The muscles of my chest tightened. "The first one, John, was the president of one of the men's co-ops. He was handsome and polite, but he wanted to be a priest. Then there was Dan—he was handsome and Jewish." I paused to see how Joan was responding. "But Dan wanted us to have sex and then get to know each other. He suggested going camping at Yosemite with a few other couples. I told him I'd never gone camping and hated bugs and was frightened of wild animals eating me. He laughed and assured me I'd be fine; he was an experienced camper. So I went camping with him and he wanted to have sex in a sleeping bag on the ground. I couldn't do that. No way." I shook my head.

I thought about lying on the hard ground in that sleeping bag by the river listening to coyotes' menacing sounds in the night and trying to understand why anyone would choose to camp out instead of being comfy in their own bed. The anxiety of camping came flooding back. I winced.

"There was no way I going to have my first sexual experience in the wild. Besides, there were other couples within earshot. I remembered hearing them groaning. I'd be damned if they were going to hear me having sex."

Both of us were quiet for a minute. I sighed.

"The trip to Yosemite was the last time you saw Dan?" Joan asked.

"It was the last time I went camping too," I said. "Jewish girls don't go camping. What was he thinking?"

I watched Joan intently, waiting for her judgment.

"Were there any other relationships in college?" Joan asked.

"Ken," I said, trying to move on from not getting a laugh about Jewish girls camping. "A Japanese-American architecture student from Hawaii." I remembered the movie *Hiroshima Mon Amour*. I'd seen it five times with Linda in high school because we both had a crush on the Japanese actor who played an architect having an affair.

"We dated a few weeks; when he held me I could feel calmness come over me..."

I thought about how he looked, or was it that actor Eiji Okada? Over the years they'd merged into one image in my mind. I imagined "him" standing in the lobby at the dorm in my sophomore year waiting for me to come out.

"He had strong, hairless arms, high cheek-bones," I smiled, remembering, "and beautiful, almost-black eyes."

I imagined kissing him. I'd felt like a piece of iron getting close to a magnet. Making out with him had been so exciting... I came when he rubbed against me.

"He told me he was falling in love with me," I said.

25

"What made you stop seeing him?" Joan asked.

"Scared I guess."

"Of what?"

"My mother would disown me...," I blurted.

My shoulders hunched over. "The night I broke up with him, my friends had a party and everyone was smoking pot. I'd never been stoned before. I don't know what I was frightened of—maybe that my mother would magically find out even though she was 3,000 miles away. But Ken encouraged me to try it and we both got stoned."

I remembered opening two chocolate kisses. The process of opening them seemed so complicated and took so long. I could hardly stand waiting to see the naked piece of chocolate. Then we smelled them for what seemed like an hour; he kissed the chocolate and then placed it in my mouth. His nails looked so pink in contrast to his dark hands.

"It reminds me of my mother's My-T-Fine chocolate pudding," I had told him. "She used to let me lick the bottom of the pot. Ah, ambrosia... Did your mother make chocolate pudding?"

"No," he had said. "She never made desserts, but my grandmother used to make *wagashi*."

"What's that?" I had asked.

"It's different kinds of cakes, all made with red bean paste."

We had both stood there examining the chocolate kisses—the shape of large drops. But something about the red bean paste made me feel that we were from different solar systems—My-T-Fine and *wagashi*.

Now, Joan broke the silence. "So, what were you afraid of?" she asked.

My attention returned to Joan. I wondered what she was thinking about me. Did she think I was a scared child? Her face showed no signs of what she might be feeling.

26

"I was afraid I could love him …"

Joan was silent.

"Disaster."

"How so?" she asked.

It surprised me that Joan didn't instantly understand.

"I imagined he was trying to make me do something I didn't want to do," I said.

"What was that?" Joan asked.

"How could I bring a Japanese-American from Hawaii back to Brooklyn to meet my mother? He wasn't Jewish; he wasn't even white. 'This is Kenji. He's from Hawaii and his parents work on a pineapple farm.' My mother would start to yell and cry. She'd be nasty. She'd say racist things to him. I can see her wailing about what her friends would say and what her sister Gus would say. She was never concerned about my happiness; it was not a consideration. But then, I don't think she ever thought about my father's either."

I thought about my father carrying a pocket knife; he never used it to gut a fish or whittle a piece of wood, but rather to clean his nails.

"His third finger had a crooked knuckle that made his small hands seem rugged, as if he had done it wrestling a bear in the forest, but he broke it playing baseball and my grandmother was too busy to take him to the doctor for a splint."

"So your mother wasn't any more concerned about your father than his mother had been," she said.

"Exactly." I shuddered with an inward sigh of relief.

My father's once curly hair was mostly gone by the time I arrived on the scene. Only wedding pictures documented its prior existence. What was left was a rim of hair that grew a few inches above his ears. He was a short man, about five foot seven, with glasses and a paunch around his waist. Some men's paunches are above the waist so they hang over their belts, but my father's was right at his waistline and his belt went around it. I smiled to myself when my mind came back to Ken and what my father might say to him. My father had a special knack for saying the wrong thing.

"My father wouldn't be overtly nasty like my mother ... ," I said. "But there was the time he started speaking in mock Chinese to the waiter in Joy Fong, the neighborhood Chinese restaurant where Jews went for Sunday dinner, and I wanted to run out in horror. Or, my father might blurt out to Ken, 'Were your parents there at Pearl Harbor?' I felt too ashamed to talk to my roommate Sue about it because she was Japanese-American. She moved in when Carole left. How could she possibly understand? Her parents were interned during World War II. She'd think I was racist. How could I explain that it wasn't racist, it was just my parents? I started a fight with Ken over something trivial—I don't even remember what it was."

I remembered we had been dancing to the Righteous Brothers. Ken's arms held me close. My head was on his shoulder; I felt his warm breath on my neck. My eyes were closed, but I cried while we were dancing.

> You've lost that lovin' feeling,
> Whoa, that lovin' feeling,
> You've lost that lovin' feeling,
> Now it's gone... gone ... gone ... wooooooh.

I wondered what Joan thought of me. I couldn't tell from the expression on her face and it made me anxious. I shifted in my seat, searching her face for some indication that she had caught me in a bit of bad behavior. But there was no smile or frown. There was no indication of a judgment, she just looked quizzical.

"So what was it you think you were afraid of?" she asked. Her voice was soft and mellow; the muscles in my back relaxed.

"If I fell in love with him and stayed with him," I said, "I would be leaving my family for good. They'd never accept him. My mother can't relate to Italians, never mind Japanese. She thought it was exotic that one of my roommates at Berkeley was Japanese-American, but that's a whole different thing than a son-in-law." I thought about Orthodox Jews who act like their children are dead if they marry a non-Jew. They mourn for them and even sit *shiva*. I thought about the rabbi at the yeshiva. He looked like the *dybbuk*, a person who was taken over by an evil demon. He wore a misshapen black suit that had chalk marks on the sleeves and around the pockets. I could imagine him sitting *shiva* for a son or daughter who married outside of the community; he was not your forgiving type. My mother wouldn't go that far, close, but not that far.

"My mother just wouldn't be able to cope with what my Aunt Gus would say. I can imagine Gus's face when she met Ken. When she disapproves of someone, she purses her lips. She has deep lines above her upper lip from years of scowling. My mother falls apart when Gus looks at her like that."

I remembered my mother and her sisters playing canasta. Aunt Gus was critical of weak players. Her name was really Augusta, but everyone called her "Gus." She signed her name in quotation marks. She sat at the table like an owl watching its prey, ready to spring on it at any moment. Every throw got a comment if it wasn't the optimal play. Gus screamed at Mitzi, "How could you throw that? What's the matter with you?"

"I once asked my mother if Aunt Gus was born sure that she was right," I explained to Joan. "She said Gus had ringworm when she was a young girl and the doctor shaved her head and all the children

29

at school made fun of her. So Gus developed an 'I don't care what you think' attitude as a defense. I used to imagine Gus convincing the children who taunted her that being bald was a fashion and they were too stupid to know it. I fantasized a whole neighborhood of children begging to have their heads shaved so they could look like Gus."

"So your mother understood why Gus was so critical of other people?"

"Yes," I nodded, "but that didn't make her any less vulnerable to Gus's criticisms."

I sat with my arms crossed wondering if Joan thought I was exaggerating my mother's reaction.

"So you were afraid of having to give up your family?" she asked.

"Yes." Her words undid a knot inside me. "I thought my relationship with Ken had potential and that frightened me."

"Unfortunately, our time is up for now," Joan said gently.

⟫⟪

The end of the session always seemed to come in the middle. I looked at Joan's face for signs of regret. Was she sorry to have to stop me midstream? There was no sign of regret on her face; I felt tears welling up. Walking out I saw a young man put away the notebook in which he'd been writing, get up and walk toward the office. I decided he was a reporter or a writer and must have interesting stories to tell Joan. From behind me she called, in her smiling voice, "Hello, Pete."

Walking home to my apartment I thought about my mother's canasta game. Hours before the Tuesday night game, my father took the bridge table and folding chairs from the hall closet in the living room and set them up. My mother took out the ornate silver pieces that were carefully stored in silver cloth bags and polished the pieces that had

30

tarnished since the last game. She took out the cut crystal, Wedgwood, and Rosenthal china from the hutch. She filled them with cashew nuts, Barton's almond kisses, chocolate peanut clusters with caramel and dark chocolate bark with raisins. When my parents were out of the house, I went to her underwear drawer, where she hid her stash under her bras, all brown under the elastic from years of wear. I took one tiny piece of chocolate bark or three cashew nuts—little enough that she wouldn't notice anything was missing. They were not for me; I stole the forbidden fruit.

Brooklyn College

I was fired from the yeshiva after two months. In the middle of a lesson about paragraph development, the head rabbi, the *rebbe*, stormed in. He was a short man with an unkempt gray and brown beard, curly gray hair and a large black mole on the top of his forehead that seemed to keep his yarmulke in place. I gasped as he came in the back door of the class and started yelling at me in broken English, "You're Eve and you've eaten the apple. They need you like a *lokh in kop*. You don't belong here. Get outta here. Out now!"

The girls were silent and kept their heads down, too frightened to look at the *rebbe*. It was as if they were each afraid of being Lot's wife turning into a pillar of salt. After all, it was as if God had struck me down right before their eyes. I felt the redness in my face and tried to hold back my tears. He stood there waiting as I packed up my books, took my coat from the back of the chair and walked out of the room— and the school.

Now I stood in front of a college classroom. The room in Whitehead Hall had a white ceiling that bore the brown stains of past leaks. It was packed with chairs with desks attached to them. The chairman of the sociology department called me in March to ask if I would take over a class for an adjunct who was sick and unable to complete the semester.

"This is an article that talks about the Electoral College.... It's related to the Dred Scott decision, which was the reading for today, because that decision was upholding something that was in the Constitution but was morally wrong," Marianne said. Her voice picked up speed as she went on. "The idea of the Electoral College that is in the Constitution is wrong too." She was like a baseball player rounding the bases. She was headed home. "The Founders created it because they didn't trust majority rule; the electors were supposed to be smarter and make more informed choices." She smiled as she slid into home plate.

I smiled in appreciation. Her ability to articulate the main point reminded me of Rifka. I got the job at Brooklyn College almost immediately after I left the yeshiva. Marianne looked a little like Rifka too—earnest brown eyes and chestnut hair. But Marianne wasn't an Orthodox Jew; she wore a gold cross around her neck had gone to a Catholic high school. She was one of the few students in the class who did the assignment properly.

The students were supposed to summarize an article from *The New York Times* that seemed relevant to the day's reading assignment and summarize it. Then they were asked to explain how it related to the reading of the day. Distinguishing between summarizing and analyzing was a challenge for them and articulating the difference was challenging for me as well. I kept repeating the same words in the definition—for instance, "A summary is when you just sum up what the article said," or "An analysis is when you don't just describe what the article said, you analyze it." Finally, I said, "A summary is a description of what is contained in an article, but an analysis is your comments on the material." But it didn't help; most of them still couldn't do it. When I took classes at Cal I dreamed about teaching in college, but the truth was that teaching at the Yeshiva was more exciting. I had introduced the girls to the modern world as if I were in the Peace Corps in Brooklyn. They were mesmerized by Simon and Garfunkel, but also had a thirst for knowledge that I knew would never be fulfilled.

Some of the college students were engaged in the discussion while a few doodled on their wood desks and some were writing in their notebooks. One young man seemed to be drawing on his hand. Jonathan, a thin pre-pubescent looking boy with thick glasses, volunteered to read his summary and analysis. The summary was fine and then he went on to the analysis.

"In my opinion, the electoral college is stupid," he said.

I smiled, identifying with his bluntness—thinking about Job being a *shmuck*.

"Jonathan, an analysis is not your opinion, it's your observation. For example, you might say the electoral college was created by the founders because they didn't trust the majority. They trusted the electors to be more educated than the average person and assumed they would make a better choice. But now, in most states the electors are all committed to vote for the candidate who carries the state, so they are not really making a choice. It takes away majority rule without replacing it with anything better."

"But isn't that just your opinion?" he asked.

My impulse was to be annoyed at him for missing the point. But then I realized he was challenging me to explain something that I had always taken for granted.

"You're right, Jonathan," I said. "But there are certain academic norms about how to express your opinion. For example, in academic discourse we don't say 'in my opinion.' We just state it and we don't use value-laden words like 'stupid,' although that may be exactly what we mean."

"So an analysis is really your opinion stated in a way that sounds objective?"

The class was laughing, but Jonathan wasn't trying to be funny—his question was sincere. I laughed too. Jonathan had exposed the hypocrisy of this academic tradition that I was struggling to uphold.

"You are absolutely right, Jonathan. It seems kind of silly doesn't it? But there are certain conventions in academic discourse and people will take you more seriously if you follow them. Also, an opinion doesn't have to be based on facts or logic the way an analysis does. Maybe that's a good way to define it—an analysis is your opinion backed up by facts or logic."

Jonathan smiled and said, "I get it. At least I think I do."

May 24, 1967

꘡꘡꘡

I planned it so I did not have to spend time in the waiting room. It was a factory and my psyche was one of the widgets. But I had to be careful because I didn't want to be late. If Joan was late, I had to wait. But if I was late, I lost part of my session. It took me years to understand the principle. Then I felt it was so unfair. I imagined stomping my foot—having a tantrum. Of course, I had never done that; my mother would have stopped that nonsense with a slap across the face.

The second door on the left opened and a tearful young girl walked out. Then I realized she was not a child, but so short that when Joan emerged behind her, the top of the woman's head only came up to Joan's breasts. Joan looked like Gulliver among the Lilliputians. I imagined the patient was crying because of the pain it caused her to be such a small person; people must treat her as if she were a child. But then, the Lilliputian was wearing a blouse with a Peter Pan collar that accentuated her childlike size. Strange. Part of her must want to be treated as a child even though she hates it, I thought. I felt sorry for her.

"Hi, Rose," Joan invited me into the consulting room with her eyes. She looked tired; her eyes didn't reflect the light as they usually did. Despite four months of treatment, I still hoped Joan would begin by talking to me.

"Say something," I said. "Please, please say something to me."

I sat with my arms crossed over my chest. I had no confidence that beneath Joan's silence was concentrated listening, no assurance that she was emotionally present. It would be years before I understood that she was keeping silent to allow me to emerge.

"Can you tell me what you're feeling?" she asked.

I imagined my mother was just inside the house, so close, and yet she might well have been in another state. If I called to her, "Mom, are you there? Mom I'm scared of the dogs.... Mom please let me come inside, I'll be good I promise," she wouldn't answer. The hopelessness turned to anger in an emotional alchemy that happened so quickly I couldn't catch it.

"I feel tortured by you," I blurted out. "It makes me so angry that I have to do it all myself. I have to open up to you when you sit there passively, showing nothing." I bit my lip, concerned that I had crossed a line.

"That's difficult. I know," she said. "But there's something about it that enrages you. There's got to be more to it, don't you think?"

"My mother never kissed me. I kissed her. I had to go to her or there was nothing. That's how it feels with you. It all has to come from me."

My throat felt sore, as if I'd been screaming. Saying it out loud soothed the ache. Silent for a moment, I rubbed my eyes. Then I moved on.

"I met this cute guy at a party, Jake. One of the other graduate students is marrying a guy who's Orthodox and he's a friend of theirs. He's a rabbinical student and wears a yarmulke."

"What about that?"

"Part of me likes the idea that he's studying to be a rabbi. A rabbi wouldn't want to have sex with me if he didn't care about me, would he?"

I thought about Jake's dark brown eyes and how serious he always seemed. It made me trust him.

"Is that something you're worried about?"

"Yes. I'm afraid of letting myself go with someone who doesn't love me." I blushed, remembering lying next to Dan in a sleeping bag in Yosemite.

"What's frightening about that?" she asked.

"Isn't that frightening to everyone?" I asked. I twisted in my seat.

"I want to understand what about it frightens you."

"It feels like I would die." I crossed my legs and uncrossed them. "It would feel humiliating. I don't know what's so upsetting about it. It just is. Aren't you Jewish?"

"What do you think?" she asked.

The blood rushed to my head; my right temple was pulsating.

"I hate when you answer my question with a question. Why don't you just answer me?"

"Well, I think you might get more out of it if we explore your feelings about my being Jewish."

I wanted to yell, but I managed to speak in a calm voice, "Don't act as if you're torturing me for my own good." I tasted the salt on my lips. "I can't stand it when you don't answer me. It feels like you're toying with me. Why don't you just answer me and then I'll tell you how I feel?"

"Okay, we could do it that way," she nodded, "or you could tell me your fantasy and I will answer you after that."

"I promise I will tell you what I imagined afterward if you answer my question," I said, rearranging myself in the chair.

"Okay, it's a deal. I'm Jewish, but I don't really observe any rituals or holidays so I'm pretty ignorant about it."

I had been holding my breath and finally let it out.

"I appreciate that. It feels much better. I imagined you were Jewish."

"Would it matter if I wasn't?" she asked.

"It makes me feel you will understand me better," I said, and then I rushed to add, "even though I know that's probably not true." I stared at the floor.

It seemed so unsophisticated, so provincial to care about such a thing, yet so core to me.

"How would my being Jewish help me understand you better?" Joan asked.

"Maybe you could understand why I would trust a rabbi."

"And I couldn't understand that," she asked, "if I wasn't Jewish?"

I knew it was ridiculous, but it mattered to me. I could read every young man's face and determine if he was Jewish. His hairline, the hair on his arm, the way he joked about his mother's cooking, were all the signs of an ethnic landscape. It was part of why I came home from California; I was an alien there. I tried to let it go and move on.

"Anyway, let me tell you about Jake, the rabbinical student I met a couple of weeks ago," I said. "I had dinner at his apartment, and I burned my hand on one of those pans he set up with an electric timer and he went to get ice. He took my hand, turned it palm up and held the ice on my thumb. He noticed the scar on the heel of my hand and asked what it was from. I told him I once put my hand through a spike. He put my hand to his lips and kissed the scar."

"It sounds like you were touched." She leaned forward in her chair.

"Yes," I said.

"What caused the scar?" she asked.

"When I was nine or ten, I punched a Spalding behind a spiked wrought-iron fence of the apartment house across the street. I climbed the fence to retrieve the ball and punched it. I impaled my hand on a spike."

"Ouch!" Joan grimaced.

"I was sure that my mother would scream at me," I said. I remembered watching through the glass door with grids as my mother rushed down the narrow hall toward me with sweat dripping down her cleavage and clothes pins in her hand. The bell had interrupted her hanging clothes on the line in the back of the house. But when she saw my hand, she ushered me into the bathroom. I remembered the sting when she poured the hydrogen peroxide on my palm and it bubbled up getting the dirt out of the wound.

"Was she sympathetic?" Joan asked.

"Well ... ," I said. I remembered sitting on the closed toilet seat as my mother put a large Band-Aid on the wound. "She didn't hug me or put her arms around me," I said, smiling. "But at least she didn't tell me it was my own fault."

"So, unlike your mother," Joan said, "Jake kissed your hand. That's why it meant so much to you."

"Yes, but he had the dinner on Friday night all set up with electric timers. Doesn't that defeat the whole purpose? Are you supposed to use timers to cook when you're not supposed to cook on the Sabbath?"

"So he responded lovingly to the scar on your hand, but it seems more important to you that he used timers to cook. What was so upsetting about that?" she asked.

It seemed so obvious to me. "The hypocrisy of it."

"What comes to mind about hypocrisy?"

"It's like the way my parents celebrated the High Holy Days." I spoke faster. "My parents and Aunt Mitzi and Uncle Ben used to share one ticket. My mother insisted that we get dressed up and walk to Ocean Parkway where we all sat on the benches across the street from the synagogue. We met Mitzi, Ben, and their kids and the adults would each take their turns going into the synagogue. Only Uncle Ben understood Hebrew, so it didn't matter when the others entered the service because they didn't understand what was going on anyway. I sat on the bench in my scratchy crinolines sweating during the inevitable Indian summer that happened every year during the High Holidays."

After a few moments of silence, she asked me what I felt.

"If there's a God why would he make it so hot on Jewish holidays? Is this what Judaism is about—sitting on a bench sweating in itchy crinolines outside the synagogue? Isn't sharing a ticket to the synagogue a sin? Why do Jews charge for tickets to synagogue on High Holidays anyway? Christians don't do that on Christmas or Easter."

"What about that?" She raised one eyebrow.

"Anyone can go to midnight mass on Christmas Eve," I said, "and put any amount they want in the plate when they pass it around. Is this what God really wants? Only Jews who can afford tickets for the High Holidays can pray?" I felt my temples pounding.

"What is so upsetting about that?" she asked.

I laughed. It was true, I didn't believe in God, so what about this was so upsetting to me? My back hurt from sitting in a chair with no support.

"My mother only cared about being able to say she went to synagogue. She didn't care about God. She didn't care about the service. She didn't know what the hell was going on. It was all in Hebrew and neither she nor my father understood it. The meaning of the High Holidays was not the point. It was just for show."

"Unfortunately, our time is up for now."

"Shit!" I mumbled.

⋙⋘

Walking out of the building, the sunshine momentarily blinded me. I put on my sunglasses and tried to stop feeling sorry for myself. I began to think about what had happened in the session. I had been able to explain that her responding to my question with a question felt rejecting, and she was willing to negotiate with me. That was a new experience.

I walked to the coffee shop where I was going to meet Jake and wondered why his tenderness over my burn was so overshadowed by him doing something I deemed hypocritical. I found Jake sipping coffee and reading *The New York Times*. It was folded lengthwise. I had learned to do that from Mr. Zamore in the fifth grade, but I had noticed over the years that most people read it above or below the crease. Only the most urbane people fold it vertically. I smiled to myself, pleased that Jake was so sophisticated.

Jake was still holding the paper when he got up and put his arms around me and held me closely. He must have just gotten out of the shower because his hair was slightly wet. He gently bit my earlobe and nibbled my neck, whispering "Hi" before he kissed me.

"How's your burn?" he asked.

"It's getting better. Thanks." I said, sniffling.

"What's making you cry?" Jake asked.

"You were thinking about me."

Jake

The elderly Black doorman opened the heavy wrought iron and glass door. He was a small, thin man with a warm smile, wearing a uniform that was a little too big for him.

"Good evenin' mam, can I help you?" he greeted me in a mild Southern accent. I imagined he recognized me from a few weeks ago and wondered what he thought of me. Was he used to an array of women visiting the rabbi on Friday nights? Or was this an unusual occurrence?

He walked me to the elevator, leaned into it and pressed the button for the sixteenth floor. Then he motioned for me to get into the elevator and said, "Have a good evening." When the door opened, Jake was standing in the doorway of his apartment smiling at me and sporting a blue and white crocheted *yarmulke* that highlighted his curly black hair. His *payos*, or sidelocks, extended to the bottom of his ear in the fashion of modern Orthodox Jews.

"*Shabbat sholom.*" He walked toward me and kissed me lightly on my mouth. His face was smoothely shaven; I smelled the Old Spice. I knew he had already gone to *Shabbat* services and returned home shortly before I arrived. I handed him the bottle of Mateus I'd brought. He laughed.

"So you've changed your ways?" he said.

Last time I had brought a bottle of Manischewitz and he had laughed at me saying, "Thank you, but did you think kosher wines have to be sweet?"

He had said it the way you might speak to a child who said something funny. I winced. My only exposure to kosher wine was on Passover and we always had Manischewitz. I had always imagined that was why Jews don't drink very much.

"There's nothing that's not kosher in wine," he had explained, "and everything is automated anyway so gentiles aren't touching it. So thankfully, we don't have to drink Manischewitz tonight."

I had always wondered what made kosher wine kosher. After all, there was no meat in it. I thought he knew all kinds of interesting things; he was so much more sophisticated than I.

When I walked into the apartment the prior time, I had noticed the silver *mezuzah* on the doorpost of the front door, because Jake kissed it as we walked in together. But this time, as I looked around and inhaled the aroma of chicken soup and garlic that drifted through the room, I realized that there was a *mezuzah* on the entrance to every room. He opened the bottle of wine, handed me a glass of rosé, and took one for himself.

"*Shabbat sholom*," he smiled and lightly touched his crystal goblet to mine.

"*Shabbat sholom*," I smiled in return. My family had never used the Hebrew greeting, but rather the Yiddish *Shabbos*, so I just repeated what he said. "Shabbat" seemed more sophisticated than "*Shabbos*." I screwed up my courage to ask him a question that further illustrated my ignorance.

"How come you have mezuzahs on the entrances to every room? We only had one on the front door."

46

He smiled and patiently explained, "No, they go on every room except the bathroom because it's so small. It symbolizes that God is keeping us safe."

The mahogany table was heavy and ornately carved with ball and claw feet. It was set with white dishes rimmed in silver. The matching chairs had upholstered seats and slightly carved arms. It felt like someone's mother's house. I didn't know any young people who had real china. My friends either had plates that came from Pier 1 or an array of plates in different patterns. Some had assorted hand-me-down chairs or Swedish modern tables with matching chairs from Bon Marché. And the only person I knew who lit *Shabbas* candles was my mother.

There was something middle-aged about Jake. He had a fellowship for his rabbinical studies, but he didn't live like a graduate student. I wondered if his parents were dead and he'd inherited the furniture and some money. A cutting board with a *challah* was on one side of the table and a vase of pink and purple tulips on the other.

An ornate silver candelabra sat on the coffee table.

"How come there are only two candles?" I asked. "My mother always lit five."

Again, he was patient as if speaking to a child.

"Well according to Jewish law, you only need to have two, but some people add more for the number of children they have. My mother lit three because I'm an only child."

"Were your parents religious?" I asked.

"Yes, they were observant, but Conservative. I wanted to be Orthodox; it feels richer to me. I thought of getting a doctorate in religious studies instead of going to rabbinical school. But I wanted to study Aramaic and I couldn't do that in a graduate program, but I can in the seminary. I love being able to read the ancient Hebrew texts that were translated into Aramaic and figuring out how the interpretation of the text has changed—it isn't literal at all. And a lot of the most interesting biblical stories were originally written in Aramaic."

His eyes sparkled from the light of the candles and he seemed more excited than I had ever seen him. I liked seeing him passionate about ideas; it made me feel close to him. I also enjoyed learning about Judaism. When I was growing up there no such thing as a bat mitzvah for girls. I had never heard of Aramaic. From what he said I figured out that Aramaic was a language that replaced Hebrew for a period.

"The chicken should be done by now. Are you hungry?" His attention had reverted from the sacred back to the profane.

"Yes. Can I help you?" I asked.

"No, everything is done." He refilled my wine glass.

I felt a little tipsy as I looked around the room at the heavy wooden bookshelves. Large leather-covered books that had Hebrew letters on them sat next to *The Last Assyrians* and *A Dictionary of Jewish Babylonian Aramaic*. On the wall next to the bookcases were two framed embroideries—one of the Star of David and the other of the burning bush; I wondered whether his parents were dead or the furniture reflected his own aesthetic. I knew he grew up in Philadelphia. With as much nonchalance as I could muster I asked, "Do your parents still live in Philadelphia?"

"Yeah, they live in the same house where I grew up."

That killed my theory about the furniture; he must have chosen it! Although he was only a few years older than me, it was hard to imagine him as a boy. I tried to conjure up an image of him in second grade. He was probably a serious child, the kind who was reading about the Civil War or memorizing facts about presidents when the other boys were reading comics. I smiled to myself thinking that as a boy he probably wore slacks or chinos pulled up ever so slightly too high while the other boys wore dungarees with the tails of their shirts sticking out.

"What does your father do for a living?" I asked.

"He owns a chain of furniture stores. That's where I got most of the things for the apartment," he said proudly.

Smiling, I noted that at least he did not actually *buy* the furniture—although he seemed to like it.

Then my mind turned to other things. I wondered if having sex was permissible on *Shabbas*. I liked the indentation in his chin and the way some of his black chest hair flowed over the top of his open shirt.

He brought me a bowl of chicken soup with a matzo ball in it. I loved having a man serve me dinner. When he put the bowl down his tongue moved from the top of my back up the length of my neck; the hairs on my neck stood up. Then he went to get his own soup and settled into his chair. He passed the *challah* and the muscles in his forearm bulged under the dark hair. Warmth spread between my legs as I ate the soup. I glanced at the oil painting of Noah's Ark with the words, "Two by two they came into the boat …" that hung prominently next to the dining area.

"Where did you get the painting?" I asked.

"One of my trips to Israel. Have you been to Israel?" he asked with a broad smile.

"No," I said. "Not yet…" I looked at the painting, avoiding his gaze. The truth was Israel came after France, England, Italy, and Spain on my list of places to visit.

After dinner he came over to my chair and nuzzled my neck, sending a shiver down my spine. I got up to help him clear the table and when I brought the plates to the sink, he put his mouth on my ear and circled the lobe with his tongue. It made me ticklish and I giggled and moved away. The room felt warm. I felt perspiration under my arms and I could hear my heart beat. He put his arm out to draw me towards him. His tongue parted my lips and I heard myself moan with pleasure. Then he pushed me toward the wall, pressing my palms with his. My arms hurt from being held up so high. He pressed against me and I felt myself twitching as he pressed his hardness between my legs. He let go of one of my hands to unbutton my blouse and started groping for my bra. But his *yarmulke* fell off and he stopped everything to pick it up. He returned it to his head and fastened it again with a single black hair pin—the kind that women used to keep rollers in their hair.

I started to laugh, but when he returned to an upright position his face was red with embarrassment and I didn't want to make him feel worse. He took my hand with his left hand and led me into his bedroom. He kissed two fingers on his right hand and touched the *mezuzah* on the way in.

The queen-sized bed was made neatly with a green duvet and matching sheets. An array of photos of Jake in Israel hung over the dark wood headboard. There was a picture of Jake at the Wailing Wall and another of him with a smiling middle-aged couple I assumed were his parents, standing next to a Bedouin with a camel.

Jake's suede *tallit* bag sat on top of the mahogany bureau, next to his parents' wedding picture in a heavily engraved silver frame.

He started kissing me and leaned on me so I fell backward onto his bed.

He took off my blouse and unhooked my bra and started to kiss my breasts circling each nipple with his tongue. Then he started kissing my neck and worked his way down my middle to my belly button where his tongue did another circular tour.

He unzipped my skirt and pulled it down along with my under-pants. Then his tongue continued its way down. I trembled and pulsated as his tongue parted my lips and slid deeper into me. I moaned with pleasure when he suddenly stopped, got up from the bed and took off his clothes. He unpinned his yarmulke and carefully put it on the side table. He took off his shirt and was wearing an undergarment that looked like a cotton undershirt with tassels at the bottom.

"What's that?" I asked him.

"It's my *tsitsit*. Don't you know what it is?" He seemed astonished that a Jewish girl wouldn't know that.

"No, I never saw one before."

He stood next to the bed naked; curly black hair covered his chest and surrounded his erection. I wondered how my mother would feel about the rabbi now. Then he fell on top of me and spread my legs with his. The contractions in my groin intensified as I clasped my legs around him. He thrust deeply, holding my hands above my shoulders. The first thrusts hurt, as if he was too big to fit inside me, but after a few lunges I seemed to loosen up. Just as I was starting to enjoy the friction, he let out a loud gasp and trembled and twitched. I assumed that meant he came; I felt a tear roll down my cheek. He let go of my hands and seemed to fall asleep. My arms ached. I moved them down to feel the curve of his spine. The sheets felt damp. *Did I wet the bed? Or worse, was there blood in his bed?* I wondered what he would feel when he realized I was a virgin. Would he be pleased or shocked? But I was relieved; I had sex and was still the same person. I no longer had virginitis.

July 17, 1967

Rushing off the elevator, I walked over to Barbara's desk to give her a check. As soon as I did, the door opened and the blond "lawyer" came out crying. She was wearing a blue summer suit—the color the Aztecs painted people, before offering them for sacrifice. They painted them and then cut their hearts out.

I wanted Joan to be glad to see me, to have thought about seeing me. I wanted her to be eager to hear what happened with Jake even though I did not want to tell her. But my desire for her interest was under constant attack from my doubts. How does she go from one person's pain to another without a break, I wondered. How will she be able to focus on me when the "lawyer" probably just told her she's thinking about killing herself?

Joan stood at the door smiling. I walked past her with a forced smile to enter the cubby. I sank into the bottomless chair. I used all my strength to push away my feeling that she was still thinking about the blond lawyer.

"I saw Jake on Sunday," I said.

"Oh," she smiled.

"I like him, but if he's is going to be an Orthodox rabbi, I want him to be genuine. I don't want him to be like my relatives sitting on the bench on Ocean Parkway. So I asked him what he thinks about *shmita*."

"What's that?" Joan said quizzically.

I crossed my arms and explained that according to religious law, Jews are not supposed to grow and sell their produce every seventh year.

"I read that it's a big issue in Israel because imagine their economy if they did that," I explained. "It's ridiculous, but if he believes in it, I want him to stick to it."

"What did he say?" she asked.

"He said, 'Of course, I believe in *shmita*. But how could Israel survive if all the farms lay fallow every seventh year?' He told me the farmers get permission from the rabbi so they can have goyim farm their land for a year. An Arab probably. It's like having a *Shabbas goy* push the button on the elevator."

Joan was silent. I wondered what she thought about all this. Was she outraged by the hypocrisy of all this? Or did she think I was silly to care about it?

"You sound angry," she said.

My eye twitched.

"Yeah. If they believe the land should lie fallow," I said in a tone that indicated it should be obvious, "they should bear the cost of what they believe in. It's supposed to be a sacrifice."

"You have pretty high standards, don't you think?" She raised one eyebrow.

"Part of me feels he's a hypocrite and part of me feels he's the most eligible man I've ever met."

"Eligible?" She scrunched her face.

"He's going to be a rabbi, for God's sake."

I started thinking about Jake's chest. I loved the way his dark hair circled around his belly and then a swath led up to his pectorals that were surrounded by curls.

54

"What are you feeling?" Joan asked.

"I don't want to tell you." We both laughed.

"How come?"

"I'm embarrassed." My cheeks were getting hot.

"Is it about sex? Is that what is embarrassing?" she asked, tilting her head to one side.

"Sex. Period!" I redistributed my weight in the chair.

"So maybe that's why you were talking about *shmita* instead?" Joan tilted her head and smiled.

"Well, maybe …" I locked my ankles.

"What is it about sex that's embarrassing?" she asked.

I felt Joan was stoking a fire, gently prodding the wood in one direction and then the next until I burst into flames.

"Come on! You know what's embarrassing about it," I said.

I remembered playing monkey in the middle during the summer with Jose, the superintendent of the apartment house across the street. I was in second grade when he became the new super. He was a handsome, muscular man, with smiling dark brown eyes, and curly black hair. He had a wife and two young children, but always made time on warm summer days to come outside after dinner to play with the kids on the block. After the game, he said he wanted to show me something. I followed him to the basement. My stomach was tight with apprehension about what he was going to show me. When we got to the darkened basement, he turned around and took my hand, putting it on his hard penis.

"Doesn't this feel good?" he said.

He moved my hand around and moaned. Excited and terrified, I ran out of the basement, crossed the street, and went into my house.

"Hi," my mother yelled from the kitchen, "wipe your feet."

I did not say a word to her.

Now, Joan said, "I'm not trying to play a game with you." She hesitated a few seconds, leaned forward in her chair and said, "I'm just trying to understand what you feel that makes it difficult for you to talk to me about sex."

I believed her.

"I've never talked to anyone about sex. No one. I talked about it theoretically, in general terms, but never exactly what I did. Okay. Here goes. I've been having sex with him. The first time I cried when he came. Maybe it was relief that I no longer have to carry the burden of being the last virgin of my generation. Maybe I cried because I imagined my mother would be happy. Having sex with a rabbi has to be okay. What could be better than bringing home a rabbi?"

"It sounds like your mother's feelings are more important than your feelings."

I stopped breathing for a moment. "What do you mean?"

"Well, you haven't said anything about how you felt about the sex. Did you enjoy it?"

I avoided her eyes and stared at the wall. I hadn't considered how I felt about the *quality* of the sex. I didn't know there were different qualities of sex. Sex or no sex—that was the question.

"Can you tell me what you're feeling?"

I was holding my breath and staring at the floor.

"Rose, what are you feeling?" she asked again.

"I don't know what to tell you." I squinted trying to read the look on Joan's face.

"What are you feeling?" she asked.

"Surprised at how stupid I am." I took a deep breath.

She cocked her head. "Did you feel I was saying you're stupid?"

"No. What I'm saying makes me feel stupid."

"Why is that?"

56

"I'm still so involved with how my mother feels about my having sex. I can't even think about how the sex feels to me. It's so stupid."

"So how *was* the sex? Did you have an orgasm?"

I sat hunched over, heart pounding and eyes closed.

"Rose?" Joan prodded.

"I don't know," I whispered.

"What do you mean?" she asked. She tilted her head and smiled softly.

"I've never had an orgasm, I don't think," I said. "So, I don't know if I had one with Jake."

There was silence for a few minutes.

"Unfortunately, our time is up for now," she said.

⟫⟪

Shaking my head as I got up, I did not look at Joan. Then shame metamorphosized into fury. I could not believe that in the middle of telling Joan about it, she ended the session! A tidal wave of rage pulled me under, arms flailing, gasping for air. I couldn't grab onto anything to steady myself.

As walked down University Place, I thought of a scene I'd witnessed a few weeks earlier at the Metropolitan Museum. It made me weep, but I had not understood why. An attractive blond woman was pushing an elderly woman in a wheelchair. The old woman was catatonic, perhaps the result of a severe stroke or dementia; she sat impassively. Yet the younger woman talked excitedly in her ear, "This is by Corot in the early nineteenth century. It's soon after the beginning of painting landscapes outside—realism." The old lady stared blankly ahead, not seeming to focus on anything, but the young woman was not deterred. She continued discussing the paintings enthusiastically.

"Look how skillfully he's shown the light on the stones...." The old woman was silent and expressionless, but the younger woman seemed confident that there was someone responsive inside the empty shell. I had felt jealous of her. I imagined there must have been an earlier time when the old woman was brimming with love and excitement and the younger woman had seen the sparkle in those now vacant blue eyes. The blond's animation came from a special place inside her where that memory lived. But I didn't have that space inside me; I had no confidence that beneath Joan's silence was interest.

When I got back to my apartment, I called Linda. Despite being separated during college when she was at the University of Wisconsin and I was at Berkeley, we were both back in New York and in constant contact.

"Do you think I might be carrying on about Jake being a hypocrite because I'm afraid of falling in love with him?"

"Well, he *is* a hypocrite, all this *Shabbas goy* stuff is ridiculous," she said, with a sarcastic laugh.

I knew Linda didn't understand how anyone could be an Orthodox Jew, but she knew me better than anyone but Joan.

"Never mind that," I said, "do you think I could be making up reasons to run away from him the way I did with Ken?"

I trusted Linda to tell me the truth.

"I think he *is* really a hypocrite; he knows you're not religious. What's he doing with you? He's never going to marry someone like you."

Part of me knew this; I didn't protest. But I still felt stabbed. Why was he so comfortable having sex with me on *Shabbas*? Because I wasn't the woman he was going to marry.

October 26, 1967

Sitting in the waiting room reading about the soldiers of the Second Battalion being ambushed by the Viet Cong, I was distracted by thoughts of Jake. He had stopped calling before Joan went on vacation in August and did not return my calls. He had ended the relationship unilaterally, abruptly. I wondered if it was because I wasn't religious or because I wasn't experienced enough in bed. Or I wasn't something else. I had been obsessing over it in all my sessions since the beginning of September.

The door opened and a tall, sullen bearded man emerged. I imagined his wife was rejecting him because he was depressed and that made him more depressed. What a conundrum. His double-breasted gray suit jacket hung off his sagging shoulders. Joan was just behind him. I had just read an article in the *Times* health section about apple vs. pear-shaped women's bodies. I decided Joan had a pear-shaped body—thick around the hips and thighs, but small breasts.

"Hi, Rose." She smiled.

The roof of my mouth just behind my tongue felt hot and raw as I sat across from her.

"Each time I leave your office," I said with my teeth clenched, "I cry all the way back to my apartment and then I do school work to try to forget how much I miss you. I'm angry now because I'm going to get into all this painful stuff and then I have to leave. I have forty-five minutes with you three times a week and I cry and rant and then you say, 'We have to stop.' What's the point?" I was Sisyphus pushing that rock up the mountain only to watch it roll down.

"You mean there's no point in telling me how you feel if you have to leave?" she asked.

"I hate those fucking self-explanatory questions. It makes me furious at you… I can't keep it in." I clenched my fists.

"What?" she asked, bewildered.

"Anger." Like a pot of soup, I kept reaching the boiling point, no matter how many times the heat was lowered.

"The effect of trying to keep it bottled up without any air," she said, "is that it makes the anger feel more toxic. When you finally express it, it comes out as a murderous rage. Right now you're telling me you feel angry. What's the problem with that?"

"You'll leave me. Like Carole. I was angry at her all the time and she left." I picked up my handbag and put it on my lap.

I remembered trying to hide my critical feelings about Carole; I had tried to say nothing. But that created a palpable tension. Sitting on my feelings made me feel stiff and awkward. I alternated between cold, tense silence and blurting out critical and angry feelings. Finally she moved out.

"I'm not leaving," Joan said. Her eyebrows rose for emphasis. "I think if you told me what I did that made you angry when it happened, it wouldn't feel so destructive. It's when you hold it in and try not to feel it that it intensifies and you blow up."

"Like Christmas vacation," I said.

"What's like Christmas vacation?" She knitted her eyebrows.

"My parents insisted I come back from California, but I had to pay for it, and then they went to Atlantic City with their friends," I explained.

"What do you mean?"

"The first Christmas at college, I had a clothing sale to raise money for my flight. I had a lot of hand-me-downs from my sister that had Lord & Taylor labels and they sold very well. Then I got home only to find out they were going to Atlantic City with their friends.

The next summer I wanted to stay in Berkeley, but my mother insisted that I come home. No clothing sale that time. I had a ride with a guy who advertised for passengers in the Daily Cal; somewhere near the Grand Canyon it became clear that the driver was expecting to have sex with me as payment for the trip. I ended up taking a Greyhound bus the rest of the way. When I got home to Brooklyn, my father kissed me, and my mother told me how bad I looked, and they went to the Jersey shore with their friends for five days."

"So ... when the session ends," she said, "you feel I don't care about all of this money and effort you have put into seeing me."

"Yes." I nodded.

"I put you out on the porch and you can't come in the house."

"Yes."

"What are you feeling?" Joan asked. Her voice was tender.

"Alone. There are dogs out there. I have to stay out there until you let me back."

Feeling angry, I had the impulse to say something that would hurt her. "That blouse is pulling on you," or "Why don't you get a better color job on your hair?" I knew this was completely irrational; it was like being angry at the maestro because the concert was going to end. But it didn't matter.

"I used to stand next to my mother with a dish towel when she washed the dishes," I said, "chanting, 'I love you true, I love you blue, I love you like glue.' She never responded." I remembered the tension in my mother's jaws and the voice of Martin Block on *Make Believe Ball-*

61

room in the background as my mother cleaned up and my father read the *Telegram*. "She'd just keep scrubbing the pan with Brillo or washing the silverware and never said a word. I used to kiss her arm because I was too short to reach her face. That's what's going on with you. I'm angry at you all the time because you don't respond, you don't love me."

Part of me understood it was completely unreasonable to expect my analyst to love me, but nevertheless I yearned for it.

Having said it out loud, I realized it wouldn't feel any better if the session were fifty minutes or an hour. However long it was, it would end at some point.

Joan was quiet.

"It doesn't matter," I said, "how I feel or what I'm in the middle of. Each session has the same rhythm even if the melody and harmony is different. I can't come back whenever I want. That's the point. I get three distinct times that I can see you and it feels like 'fuck me' in between time. I wrote something yesterday. I want to read it to you."

"Yes, go ahead."

I took out the folded paper from my purse and read the typed page I'd written the day before:

> The three-year-old that lives with me told the twenty-three year-old that lives with me: "If she loves her, she doesn't love me." The twenty-three-year-old said to the three-year-old, "That's silly; you're acting just like a three-year-old." But the three-year-old, being mature for her age said: "I *am* three years old. I hate her because she loves her more than she loves me." But the twenty-three-year old said: "Just because she loves her doesn't mean she doesn't love you. Why don't you tell her you feel rejected?' "But," said the three-year-old, "if I tell her I feel

rejected and she *is* rejecting me then imagine how awful that would be." The college professor had a hard time understanding this convoluted logic, but then turned to the three-year-old and said: "But I don't understand. Then you will always feel rejected because you would rather feel it *all the time* than take a chance on finding out it is true *sometime*s?" The three-year-old responded: "Yes, it's better to have nothing and hope for everything than to have something and know there is nothing else coming."

"Who's the 'her'?" she asked.

"I don't know. Maybe your other patients... or maybe my Aunt Gus. I don't know if my mother loved my aunt Gus, but pleasing her sure took precedence over anything concerning me. I wanted my mother to stop doing the dishes or talking on the phone or worrying about what my aunt thought," I said, "and look at me."

"Do you feel I don't look at you?"

"No, I don't feel that when I'm here with you, but when the session ends it feels so cold and uncaring. No matter what I am feeling or talking about—we have to stop. I can't seem to get over that hump."

"Because it feels so much like your mother shutting the door behind you?"

It was as if I'd been waiting for her to put those two wires together and now that she had, I lit up.

"Yes, that's exactly how it feels. I have to fend for myself..."

"We're going to have to stop in a few minutes. But I want to talk to you about changing my office. I'm going to be leaving the clinic and practicing only in my office uptown. Do you feel that you want to continue working with me at my office?"

I straightened up and looked at her. Her eyes looked concerned as if she was actually not sure if I would want to leave the clinic with her. "Yes, of course I want to continue working with you," I said. I wanted to scream at her: *How can you even ask me that?*

"Great!" She smiled. "Starting in two weeks, we will have the same appointment times, but meet at my office uptown. This is the address." She leaned across to hand me a printed piece of paper with her address on it.

Her right hand brushed my arm before I took the paper. I'd taken something forbidden like the tin of chocolate-covered almonds my mother used to keep in her underwear drawer.

Her voice was matter of fact when she said, "Our time is up for now."

My head hung like a dead sunflower. It took me a moment to gain my composure and push up out of the canvas chair. I left the room without looking at her.

⬗⬗⬗

Startled when she ended the session, I felt slapped. When my mother slapped me across the face, I gritted my teeth. It hurt, but I was braced for it. I started every session with that tension in my shoulders, wanting to be prepared for the slap, but then inevitably Joan would understand something I was ashamed of or make a connection that soothed me and a wave of loving feelings would wash over me. The tension drained out of me. Then the session would end and I'd feel slapped again. But this time she tried to prepare me for the end; it wasn't her fault that her hand happened to touch mine.

I met Linda for coffee on University Place, around the corner from the clinic.

She kissed me hello as I walked up to her.

"I spent my whole session angry at Joan because the sessions always end."

"What? I don't understand." She scrunched her face.

"Well, no matter how I feel, I have to leave after forty-five minutes."

"It's your separation anxiety. You know how you used to feel when you had to leave my house and go home for dinner. You would call me as soon as you got home. Or when you slept over at my house and then left to go to work at the beauty parlor. You had to drag yourself out. It's the same thing."

I remembered when I got a job at Bill's Coffee Shop on Church Avenue to pay for the cigarettes and lunches with Linda. I earned tips by bringing coffee and lunches to the women in the beauty parlor on Saturdays. I made a deal with Bill—I brought all my orders to him in exchange for free Marlboros. Most of the women having their hair coiffed were Jewish and they didn't allow their hair to get gray; no matter how wrinkled their faces, their hair was blond or frosted or auburn. Gray hair, like pork, was against their religion.

They sat under big metal dryers that made them look like Martians all lined up in a row—unless you pulled the dryer up to expose the rollers underneath. I imagined them landing in outer space and walking on a pock-marked planet. The loud whirring noise from the row of dryers made it impossible to get their orders for coffee or Danish or a tuna on rye with lettuce and tomato.

One Saturday I walked around with my pad and pencil silently gesturing that I was taking orders for breakfast or lunch. Mrs. Steinberg, a heavy-set woman who sat with her legs spread apart, like men on the subway, turned off the dryer with the switch hanging next to the dryer. She pulled up her heavy helmet and searched for her purse.

"Here you are darling," she said as she handed me a five-dollar bill. Mrs. Steinberg was a good tipper—she made no effort to give me the correct change.

"Thank you, Mrs. Steinberg," I said.

"I'd like a tuna sandwich on rye toast with lettuce and tomato," she said.

I nodded and dutifully noted it.

"And a Coke with a lemon," she added.

"Yes, of course," I said.

Mrs. Steinberg smiled, carefully pulling her dryer over the large rollers in her hair.

Now I smiled at Linda across the table.

"So, have you heard from Jake?" she asked.

"No, the bastard just stopped calling."

"Are you okay about it?" Linda asked, tilting her head.

"I just realized what the session was about," I said. "I was angry at Joan because the session always ends, but it's was Jake who ended things abruptly, not Joan." I scrunched up my face.

"Yeah," Linda said stretching her arm out to take my hand.

December 8, 1967

The walls of the elevator in Joan's building were mahogany; it was an elegant cocoon, completely different than the cold, automated elevator at the clinic. I had been coming to sessions at Joan's apartment for a month, but still I wondered what the elevator operator thought of me. I was sure he didn't know anyone in therapy other than these strangers on the elevator. A short, thin, balding man, he had a boyish appearance except for the white rim around his head. I imagined he lived in a working-class ethnic neighborhood in Brooklyn or Queens—his sons firemen or policemen, and his daughters housewives married to firemen and policemen.

Joan's small square waiting room had four doors and very little wall space. The double doors on the right led to the office. I assumed the other doors were entrances to her apartment and maybe a closet. The only picture on the wall was a watercolor of an English country house with different shades of yellow sunlight reflecting off it. On the lamp table, next to the magazines for patients to thumb through while they were waiting for their sessions, was a metal ash tray that said, "Things always come in mixed packages." It was such a simple idea and yet I found it so hard to accept.

The door opened and a heavy woman in a brown tweed suit and comfortable shoes walked out. I'd never seen this woman before. Her eyes were puffy under her glasses as if she'd been crying. Her thin black hair hardly covered her scalp; sweat made her bangs stick to her forehead. I imagined she was a professional, maybe a doctor, and she was talking about how lonely she was because men weren't interested in her. I wondered what Joan said when "the doctor" begged her for reassurance that she would find a man to love her. I smiled to myself thinking that she hummed, "Whatever will be, will be, the future's not ours to see, Que será, será."

That was too nasty, Joan would never do that. Maybe she said, "You're a bright, lovely woman. If you do the things you love, you'll find someone who loves them too and when he gets to know you he will love you as well." I imagined her tone—so soft and mellow it brought the patient to tears. Or perhaps she said in that same tone, "You have so much love to offer, I'm sure you'll find a man who wants that and can appreciate what a bright and interesting person you are."

Teary, I was lost in my daydream about Joan's compassion for "the doctor." But then I started thinking about Ken and Jake. It was clear by now that Jake had never been interested in a serious relationship with me. He had sex with me because I wasn't religious—because he would never consider marrying someone like me. Linda had told me that and she was right. But Ken had been in love with me and I worried that I'd squandered my opportunity. I remembered the warmth of his body when he rubbed against me, the way he sang in my ear when we danced to Herman's Hermits. "Baby, baby, can't you hear my heartbeat?"

Joan greeted me. "Hello, Rose, come in." I followed her into her spacious living room with built-in book shelves under a wall of windows overlooking a park. A large rectangular glass vase filled with opulent white flowers sat on the top of a bookcase. On each side of it were fern plants—one had solid green leaves while the other had variegated leaves with white flecks on them. On the right side of the room, against the wall, was a couch without arms for patients, and against the left wall was a loveseat with arms. Above the couch was a Georgia O'Keeffe print of a large white calla lily. Joan sat in a leather recliner behind the couch, her back to the windows. Next to her chair, in the corner, was a thriving floor plant in a large blue ceramic pot. I sat on the couch.

The room at the clinic was tiny, but I was close enough to touch Joan. Now there was a football field between us.

"I feel far away," I said, crossing my arms. I looked around the room at the shelves lined with books whose bindings were cracked from having been read with gusto, a rug with an American Indian design that looked as if it might have been bought in Santa Fe or someplace else in New Mexico or Arizona. The realization of how much I didn't know about her life washed over me and it made me feel lonely. But the wish to know more about her, to be closer to her, was almost immediately transformed, as if the atoms realigned themselves in a chemical reaction, into feeling exiled and resentful.

"I feel angry at you," I said, shrugging my shoulders. "What else is new?"

We both chuckled.

"Did you ever read the children's book about Bugs Bunny and his carrot machine?" I asked.

"No. What's making you think of that now?" she asked.

"Well, he would put all kinds of things in the machine and they would all come out as carrots. That's what I do. I have a whole variety of feelings about you: hopefulness, yearning, disappointment, distance, and they all come out as anger. I keep repeating the same thing."

"Well, you know analysis is like writing a symphony." She chuckled. "It involves repetition plus variation."

The tightness seeped out of the muscles of my neck. I put my hands on my lap.

"So why are you angry at me?" she asked.

Part of me responded to the gentleness in her voice—the invitation to join her. Her voice was like a warm bath. I wanted to climb in and let all tension flow out of my body, but another part of me stubbornly held on to my litany of complaints: the room felt too big, it wasn't cozy. The fabric on the loveseat was nubby and irritated the back of my thighs.

"You're so special to me and I'm just one of many people you see. Your life is a huge mural and I am just a speck of paint on the edge."

I waited her to say something.

"How does that speck of paint feel?" she asked.

"Small. There are so many parts to the mural—it's full of people and flowers and books. But I'm such a small speck all the way at the edge."

"Did you ever read *The Little Prince*?" she asked.

The question seemed to come from nowhere. "I read it in high school French class," my voice was stilted, "but I got a 65 in French, so I didn't understand it very well."

She got up from her recliner to get the book from the bookcase. She'd never gotten out of her chair during a session before. Then she walked over to me to show me the picture. I was breathless. Casually, she put on her reading glasses that were hanging around her neck and returned to her chair. She opened the book and began to read aloud:

> He was standing before a garden, all a-bloom with roses.
> "Good morning," said the roses.
> The little prince gazed at them. They all looked like his

flower. "Who are you?" he demanded, thunderstruck.

"We are roses," the roses said.

And he was overcome with sadness. His flower had told him that she was the only one of her kind in all the universe. And here were five thousand of them, all alike, in one single garden!

Then he went on with his reflections: "I thought that I was rich, with a flower that was unique in all the world; and all I had was a common rose." And he lay down in the grass and cried.

The little prince went away, to look again at the roses. "You are not at all like my rose," he said. "As yet you are nothing. No one has tamed you, and you have tamed no one. You are like my fox when I first knew him. He was only a fox like a hundred thousand other foxes. But I have made him my friend, and now he is unique in all the world."

"So what do you think?" Joan asked. She tilted her head slightly and smiled.

She seemed so much more relaxed in her own office than she had been at the clinic. But part of me worried that she'd had a stroke or something. It was so out of character for her to pick up a book and start reading it to me. But I didn't want to do or say anything that might discourage her. I was afraid to make a sound or move. It was like snuggling next to my mother while she was asleep. I didn't want to wake her.

"I want to feel that—I'd like to feel that you've tamed me and I don't have to be your only patient to be special to you."

She continued to read.

> To be sure, an ordinary passerby would think that my rose looked just like you—the rose that belongs to me. But in herself alone she is more important than all the hundreds of you other roses:... because it is she that I have listened to, when she grumbled, or boasted, or even sometimes when she said nothing. Because she is my rose.

"But the situation is a little different," I said. "I want to be your special rose, but you have all these other roses. That's what makes me so angry—you have all these other roses."

"The point is that it doesn't matter how many roses there are," she said. "What makes a rose special is the process of taming—listening when you grumble or boast or say nothing. It's the process of understanding and working through that we do together that makes our relationship special. It can't be compared to any other. It doesn't matter how many others there are. What happens between you and me is special and that's what matters... But we are going to have to stop."

>>><<<

Like the aftermath of a downpour, the room was still. Joan had given me something that I could take with me. I didn't feel lonely when I left. I walked to the subway pondering what Joan said. "Analysis is like a symphony; it requires repetition and variation." Only Joan could understand the shifts that were occurring in me; the variation could only be discerned if you were familiar with the repetition.

Walking down West End Avenue, I thought about Linda's mother, Dorothy. She had introduced us to the writing of Herman Hesse and Ayn Rand. I didn't realize it then, but those books were about the proper place of the self—from Siddhartha's obliteration of the self to Ayn Rand's worship of the self. Certainly, this was a central concern for Linda and me and it seems that it was for Dorothy as well.

> In the shade of the house, in the sunshine of the river-bank near the boats, in the shade of the Sal Woods for-est, in the shade of the fig tree is where Siddhartha grew up, the handsome son of the Brahmin, the young falcon, together with his friend Govinda, son of a Brahmin.

I saw Linda as Siddhartha and myself as Govinda. I was a follower. I was following Linda on a spiritual quest and part of my idealization of her had to do with her mother. Perhaps I imagined Dorothy to be the wise ferryman who took me across the river and transformed me the way Vasudeda was instrumental in Siddhartha's journey.

"I thank you Vasudeva," said Siddhartha, "for listening to me so well! These people are rare who know how to listen. And I did not meet a single one who knew it as well as you did. I will also learn in this respect from you."

January 26, 1968

I sat in the tiny square waiting room. On one side were the double doors that led to Joan's living room/office. Opposite the office doors was a door to her apartment and directly in front of me was another. Her *real* life was through those doors. The double doors opened, and the blond "lawyer" emerged with a smile on her face. Instead of turning left and going out the front door, she opened the door leading to Joan's apartment. I gasped silently, stifling the impulse to yell, "You can't go there." Then I realized that was the hall leading to the bathroom. I'd been having my sessions in Joan's apartment for three months, but I hadn't asked to use the bathroom. Sometimes I left the office and stood with my legs crossed on the elevator, trying to control myself until I got to the coffee shop around the corner. Asking to use her bathroom was embarrassing, as if urinating, and certainly defecating, would disgust her. "You shit?" I imagined her exclaiming in horror. Patients, I realized at that moment, were allowed to go through that door and turn right to go to the bathroom. Joan followed a minute later and greeted me.

I heard the toilet flush as Joan closed the double doors behind me.

"It feels strange coming here—I still feel like I'm intruding," I said. I picked up my purse and hugged it.

"Can you tell me about that?"

No, I couldn't. I didn't want to insult her by complaining about her using her oversized living room as an office or the nubby fabric on her couch.

"It's your house," I said. "Your painting on the wall ... It feels like I'm seeing things I shouldn't be seeing."

"What comes to mind about seeing things you shouldn't be seeing?"

"You think it's sexual, don't you?" I asked. I couldn't decide what was worse: thinking something sexual and having to tell her, or not thinking something sexual and having to tell her.

"When my parents went out, I told you, I used to go to my mother's underwear drawer to check out the chocolate stash. More though ... Like a toy store and the owner went out for an hour or two. I could open all the cases and try out all the toys. I found some condoms."

"How did you feel about that?" she asked.

I thought about my mother's underwear—the elastic that had stretched from so many washings.

"I couldn't believe it in a way. I could imagine my father having sex, but I couldn't imagine my mother."

"What about that?"

"The only time I ever saw my mother as a sexual person was when she would sometimes talk on the phone to my aunt or one of her friends. If she were really involved in the conversation, she would sometimes stroke herself and smell her finger. She clearly liked her aroma...."

"You mean your mother would masturbate when she was on the phone?" She sounded surprised.

My head jerked and my eyes widened. "I never thought of it that way. It was just something she did...." I bit the inside of my cheek.

"I think on some level you knew what she was doing because you thought of it when I asked you about your mother's sexuality."

My stomach tensed. "I guess so. But it didn't have to do with another person...."

"Well, yes, that's what masturbating is about. Pleasing yourself. Do
you masturbate?" Her tone was casual as if she were asking, Do you eat
cereal for breakfast?

I stared at the windows. "You know it's hard to talk about this stuff
and look at you. I'm looking in every direction to not look at you," I
said.

"Maybe you want to use the couch?"

I imagined lying on the couch looking at the ceiling; it had this
popcorn looking stuff on it. Then I wondered what I would do about
my shoes. Should I take them off or just be very careful that the soles
never touched the couch?

"That might feel really weird," I said. I fidgeted with the strap on
my purse.

"Well," she said wrinkling her chin, "you can try it for a few sessions and if you don't like it you can change your mind."

I got up from the loveseat and walked over to the couch. I worried
about the shoe problem. There was a piece of fabric at the foot of the
couch. I wondered if that meant I didn't have to take off my shoes. I
took off my shoes and lay down.

"What are you feeling?" Joan asked.

My left stocking had a run at the ankle and I was embarrassed that
she was going to notice. I tried to hide it by putting one foot behind
the other, but the gash peeked out from the inside of my ankle. I needed to hide both the run and the fact that it bothered me. I twisted my
foot to find a concealing angle but then I got a cramp in my foot. My
toes were curled and paralyzed. I blurted "Ouch," and jumped up from
the couch to try to walk it off.

Joan laughed. "What's going on? Is this a reaction to my asking you about whether you masturbate?" she asked.

She remembered where we had left off. I stuttered, "No... it wasn't that..." My foot still hurt.

Hesitating for a moment, I tried to decide which was more embarrassing, confessing to trying to hide a run in my stocking or trying to avoid talking about masturbating. I opted for the run in my stocking.

"Actually, I was hiding the run in my stocking and I moved my foot awkwardly and got this muscle contraction."

Joan laughed and shook her head in mock disbelief.

"What would make you hide the run in your stocking? What would it mean if I saw it?" she asked.

"It's really ridiculous," I said going back to the couch, "now that we're talking about it, but some part of me feels that having a run in my stocking exposes me in some way. It allows you to see a part of me that I have no control over."

"I think this is about masturbating not the run in your stocking. Don't you?" She was smiling.

Chuckling, I said, "Yes, I guess so. Well ...I touch myself, but I don't have an orgasm. I guess I think of 'masturbating' as meaning you come." I crossed my legs.

"Not necessarily. Do you have any fantasies when you masturbate?"

"No, I don't have any fantasies," I said.

"You sound frightened."

Her voice was soft, but my temples tightened as if my head were in a vise.

"Something is wrong with me and you're going to uncover it now." I held my head as still as I could.

"Actually," Joan said, "I think you're afraid that nothing's wrong with you and both you and your mother are sexual women. But I wonder what it is about that that frightens you?"

I was speechless for a moment. I locked my arms.

"Our time is up. We're going to have to stop for now."

⋙⋘

For once I didn't mind leaving. I suddenly realized there was more than one way of feeling known. One way felt consoling and engendered closeness and gratitude. The other way felt exposing and scary—there was something about me that Joan and I were going to discover and it was going to change the way I saw myself in some fundamental way. I wanted to change, and yet a part of me held on to my image as a tomboy. It was as if I'd been singing the same song for years and Joan was offering a new arrangement.

As I walked out of her office into the waiting room, I noticed the tall vase with white lilies. They were so dramatic—grand silky blooms with orange spikes protruding from pristine white petals. I inhaled the spicy fragrance that emanated from them and smiled to myself. Then I thought about Dorothy, Linda's mother. She always had fresh flowers in her house in contrast the plastic ones my mother had. And in lieu of a *shmata* like my mother wore at home, Dorothy `wore skin-tight pants and sexy sweaters. Her eyes were outlined in black and her lips were red. She tossed her long brown hair when she talked passionately.

Dorothy and her husband Harold, who had been her psychoanalyst when she was married to Linda's father, started an affair during the treatment which resulted in Linda's parents' divorce. My eyes had widened and my mouth dropped when Linda told me the story. I thought that explained why someone as sexy as Dorothy was with Harold. He was twenty years her senior, had liver lips, a pot-belly and wispy gray hair. But he spoke in a cultured tone and had an old-world charm and dry wit.

Dorothy turned the enclosed front porch into an art studio. She painted with a knife rather than a brush and all the paintings were thick with paint. She painted recognizable flowers and vases and people; they were not abstract. Harold's consultation room was across the entry hall from Dorothy's sunny studio and it had big white folding doors that were thick with soundproofing. Students came for art lessons with Dorothy, and psychiatric patients passed them on their way in and out of Harold's office.

During the summers in high school, when Linda was in Connecticut at Buck's Rock "work camp" playing guitar and singing Woody Guthrie songs, and I was working as a cashier at Schrafft's, or later, as a waitress at the Hotel New Yorker, I often stopped in to talk to Dorothy.

One hot July afternoon, a few months before my sixteenth birthday, I stopped by her house. Dorothy was sitting in the living room in a bikini, sipping a gin and tonic with a piece of lime in it. Her hair was wet from taking a swim in the backyard pool. I smiled to myself, thinking about my mother's bathing suit—a one-piece with a skirt around the bottom to hide her protruding belly.

Dorothy was writing one of her letters to Linda. Twenty years older than Linda, she wrote yearly letters intended for Linda to open when she was the same age as Dorothy at the time of writing. She wrote them with her Mont Blanc fountain pen in beautiful script, and carefully sealed each one in a scented envelope with her age on the front. I was jealous that Linda's mother gave so much thought to their relationship, in contrast to my mother, who seemed to only think about me when I did something that irritated her. It never dawned on me that she was preparing to be absent when Linda opened those letters. I never asked myself why Dorothy needed to write letters to be opened later.

As I sank into an overstuffed chair, I could smell the sweetness of the yellow Asiatic lilies in a cylinder-shaped glass vase on the coffee table. I started talking about the book I was reading, *The Stranger* by Albert Camus.

"Do you want some iced tea?" Dorothy asked.

"Yes, thanks."

I got up and followed her into the kitchen and watched her open the refrigerator and take out the container of iced tea. I talked as I watched her take the tall glass out of the cabinet, put the cubes in the glass, and pour the tea. She handed it to me and I followed her back into the living room. She sat down on the couch and started licking the envelope containing the letter she had just finished.

I went on talking. "People are so presumptuous about how you feel about your mother. They always assume you love your mother. Your mother dies and they say: 'Oh, you must have loved her so much.' You know Camus starts the book with: 'Mother died today.' And then he goes to this restaurant and the owner says to him, 'There's no one like a mother.' What does *that* mean?" I asked rhetorically.

Dorothy finished licking the envelope and wrote "Linda 36" on the front and put it down. "Isn't that the point—the triteness of the response?"

"Oh, you mean the whole book is about meaninglessness and the trite remark is meaningless?"

"Well, it's actually both meaningless and profound," she continued. "On one level it's a trite remark and yet on another level it's true. After all, no one affects you more than your mother—whether she's good or bad. My mother certainly affected me even if I've spent my life trying to be the opposite of her."

I knew from Linda that Dorothy's mother was a sweet old Jewish lady; surely Linda's grandmother would never have ridden on motorcycles wearing black leather pants like Dorothy.

"Wow, that's a scary thought," I blurted out. "I don't want to be like my mother. I don't want to spend my life washing the floor and screaming at everybody. But I can't escape her. If I spend my life trying to be the opposite of her she still will have shaped me."

Dorothy nodded her head in agreement, and then Phil the pool man came in through the back door wearing cut-off jeans and a T-shirt. He was carrying a tall plant with large red flowers in a black plastic container. He looked at Dorothy and said,

"Do you want the hibiscus in the ground? Because it won't survive the winter that way."

Dorothy got up excitedly to greet him, putting her hand on his muscular hairy arm, and began commiserating about the hibiscus. Our conversation abruptly ended. I'd been sitting in the sun feeling the warmth and suddenly the clouds rolled in and I started to shiver. I don't think she noticed when I quietly picked up my shoulder bag, said "good bye" under my breath, and hurried out the front door.

March 5, 1968

Waiting for my session to begin, I was grading an essay by Esther, an orthodox Jewish student in my Introduction to Sociology class at Brooklyn College, and I started to think about Frume. Esther could attend college after graduating from a yeshiva—perhaps her family was not as orthodox as Frume's. Esther seemed content. She was married, but spoke lovingly of her husband, so I assumed, rightly or wrongly, that it was not an arranged marriage.

Suddenly I heard a dog bark from inside the apartment and then the double doors to the office opened, and the perfectly dressed blond "lawyer" came out. The lawyer was wearing beautiful orange coral earrings that accentuated her blond hair and porcelain skin. I imagined she went to the gym every day to work out before she went to the office. She was probably married to another high-powered lawyer. I pictured her buying a cappuccino every morning on the way to the gym because she was too lazy to make coffee at home.

Joan greeted me with, "Hi, Rose." She was wearing a beautiful black velvet scarf that shimmered purple in the light. I wondered if it was a gift from "the lawyer," because I had never seen her wearing a scarf before.

Feeling envious of "the lawyer" and upset about the dog, I focused on the crown molding around the ceiling; I tried to meditate on it so I could let the bad feelings go. Exhale. Let it go....

"I read this book about oneness and separateness by Louise Kaplan," I said, settling myself on the couch. "She says we all want oneness to different degrees, and we go through stages of separation, but we regress back to the wish for oneness. That's me." I nodded. "Some people spend their lives seeking oneness with God; I'm after it on earth. I didn't know that's what I was after. It's about oneness when I want a friend to know, when they call, that I'm sick or I've just had a fight with my mother; when I want a man to know that he should touch me this way and not that way without my having to tell him. I feel angry that you or they don't respond as if they knew. Now I get it. My wish for the other person to know without having to tell them, is a wish for oneness. I get it. It makes me wish I had a different mother. I've always wanted a different mother."

"Really," she said, "tell me about it." Her voice was inviting.

"Well, of course there was Dorothy. She was always playing Jimmy Durante's version of The September Song. I still sing that song to myself walking down the street sometimes. I don't know why it has stuck in my mind all these years. Do you know how it goes?"

"Why don't you sing it for me?"

"I have a terrible voice, but it goes like this":

Oh it's a long while
From May to December
But the days grow short
When you reach September....

I stopped and made a faux cough.

"Maybe it felt as if your days would grow short when you reached September."

I laughed.

"You mean," I said, "when September came Linda would be back and I'd be back in school and I wouldn't have Dorothy all to myself?"

"Exactly," she replied.

I started thinking about the dream I had that morning about Joan. I was afraid it was a sexual dream; I didn't want to tell her about it. "When I was a kid," I said, "I wasn't interested in playing with girls; I wanted to do everything the boys did."

I remembered playing stoop ball with Philly Kornfeld and Gerard Rizzetti. We stood on the sidewalk and threw the ball at the steps—one hundred points for hitting the tip of the step and catching it on a fly; ten points for hitting the middle of the step and catching it on a fly, and five points for catching it on a bounce.

"Are you saying you're afraid you are a lesbian?" Her inflection implied that it was an unnecessary anxiety. She was trying to reassure me too fast.

"I think I have penis envy," I blurted out. "I used to stand in front of a mirror and practice putting a crease in the fly of my dungarees in the same place as Philly Kornfeld's crease. The crease wasn't from his penis, but from his tugging at it all the time. It wasn't an option for a girl. It was one of the privileges of being a male—like peeing in the street instead of having to climb the steps and go to the bathroom. None of the boys on our street had to leave the game and go upstairs to pee. I wanted a crease in my pants."

"Are there any other reasons you're concerned you might be a lesbian? Have you ever had a sexual experience with a girl or a woman?"

I noticed Joan's tone had changed. She wasn't treating my anxiety so lightly. She was asking about whether there was some reason to be worried about it. My temples were pounding.

"I've never had a sexual encounter with a girl or a woman, but I have these intense relationships with women. There was my Aunt

Hannah. Gus made me feel there was something wrong with me for loving Hannah. And there were Linda and Dorothy in high school and then Carole in college. And I worry about how much I care about you. I love you. Does that mean I'm a lesbian? I seem to be obsessed with you. I'm either here, waiting to get here, worried about having to leave, or depressed because I had to leave."

"Do you have any sexual fantasies about me?"

My chest tightened.

"They're not directly sexual," I said. "But I had a dream about you and I was lying next to you in a bed. That scared me. I'm afraid to tell you about it."

"You're afraid you have sexual feelings about me?" she asked.

"Yes," I sighed. I folded my hands on my lap.

"What's scary about having sexual feelings about me?"

"Oh come on," I yelled, "you know damn well what's scary about it." I was silent for a few moments. "I don't want to be a lesbian," I said in a calmer voice.

"You mean if you have any sexual feelings about me it means you're a lesbian?"

I had been holding my breath and exhaled.

"Yes."

"People have all different kinds of sexual feelings. It doesn't necessarily mean you're a lesbian. They're just feelings."

"Are you saying," I asked very slowly, "that heterosexuals have homosexual feelings?"

"Sure. Why wouldn't you have sexual feelings about both men and women? Who you actually want to have sex with is a different issue from having sexual feelings."

"You mean I might have sexual feelings about you, but not want to actually have sex with you?"

"Yes, of course." She sounded so matter of fact. "You don't have any control over your feelings, but you have control over your actions. But why don't we just explore your feelings first?"

The tightness in my shoulders relaxed. For the first time, I noticed how sensuous the gray fabric was behind the large white flower in the Georgia O'Keeffe poster.

"Can you tell me what you're feeling?"

"I feel calmer. Relieved."

"When did you have the dream?"

"This morning."

"Before our session?"

"Yes, I felt so sad when I left here yesterday. I had a magnet in me that kept pulling me back here. It was so exhausting to keep pushing myself forward because this force was pulling me back."

"So why don't you tell me what happened in the dream?" Joan asked.

"It was a military or hospital dormitory with cots on both sides of the room. I was lying in one of the cots next to you."

"Does anything come to mind about a room with cots on both sides of the room?" she asked.

"Well, there was no privacy. There were all these cots that other people slept in. They just weren't there right then."

"What comes to mind about that?"

"Well, I lie on this couch in your office that looks like a cot. Other people lie on it before me and after me. Lots of people lie on it." I bit my lip.

"So it's not special," Joan said.

"No, I'm not special. I can't really be close to you."

"But in the dream you are close to me?"

"Yes, in the dream, it's just the two of us," I said.

"What about lying on the cot with you? Did we touch each other?"

"We were snuggling, it felt good—safe and comfortable."

"Were you aroused?"

I crossed my arms and then uncrossed them. "No, I just felt close to you."

"Does anything come to mind about lying next to a woman?"

"Yes. I remember lying next to my mother while she was taking a nap. I'd be very quiet and lie on my father's side of the bed and listen to her breathing. But, on weekend mornings when I was little I climbed into my parents' bed and snuggled with my father and played with the hairs on his chest and rubbed my cheeks against his day old whiskers. I never went to my mother's side of the bed."

"Unfortunately, our time is up for now."

※

The dream didn't seem to be sexual. I probably wasn't a lesbian; it was about wanting to be close to a woman, but not sexually. As I walked down Broadway toward the subway, I thought about Linda and Dorothy. I had been so jealous of Linda's close relationship with her mother—until Linda's Sweet Sixteen party.

The party was at Waikiki Wally's in Manhattan. It had been a big party with a live band and I was jealous because my sixteenth birthday had been celebrated at home with a cheesecake from Junior's.

Dorothy was wearing a tight, low-cut black dress and more makeup than usual. She kept downing those pineapple drinks with tiny umbrellas. Dorothy was getting drunk and talking fast and loud. Then Dorothy "broke in" when Linda and her boyfriend, Clay, were dancing. Linda tried to cover up her embarrassment and graciously offered Clay's hand to her mother who proceeded to pull him close to her.

What is she doing? I walked over to Linda and tried to divert her attention, but she kept turning her head to look at Clay and Dorothy. Dorothy was putting her head on his shoulder and he was dancing stiffly to try to make clear that he was not encouraging her.

After the party, I became suspicious of Dorothy's most avid student, Christopher, who was a balding Classics professor 10 years younger than Dorothy. He took art lessons every day after his classes at Columbia and I could tell he was in love with her. He cooed in delight at every word she said. He looked at Dorothy as if he was a little boy in love with his mother.

Linda called me the day after the Sweet Sixteen and said she needed to talk and asked me to come to her house. I knew something bad had happened. I was the one who was always calling her and needing to talk to her; she never needed to talk to me. As I sat on the subway, I imagined all the things that could have happened that she wouldn't want to say on the phone. If Harold or her father were sick or died she would have told me on the phone. Maybe she broke up with Clay; maybe she caught Dorothy having sex with Christopher. I ran the few blocks from the subway station to Linda's house.

I pushed open the heavy glass-paneled door and breathlessly ran up the steps to Linda's room. She was lying on her bed crying in the pillow.

"What happened?"

"She ran off with Christopher. Can you believe it? She just left without a note and then called to say she's in Cape Cod with him."

April 17, 1968

On my way to the train at Union Square, I thought about Joan. I loved the way she was able to follow the threads of what I was saying even when I had no clue about the underlying theme of my associations. I admired her ability to, at least most of the time, keep her cool even when I raged at her. I wanted to be able to do that. The classroom part of my doctorate in sociology was finished and I planned to be a professor. I knew I could have an impact on my students' lives, but I'd never be able to affect them the way that Joan was changing my life. So I started thinking about becoming a psychoanalyst. On the way to the subway, I stopped at Washington Square Institute to pick up a brochure about their training program.

The express train was pulling out when I got to the subway station after my detour and I had to wait almost 15 minutes for the next one. I ran most of the way from 96th Street to 99th Street, but was still 10 minutes late when I arrived at Joan's office. I had rarely been late in the two years I had been seeing her because I hated it. I lost the time from the session even if I was delayed by something out of my control.

When I opened the door to the waiting room, the door from Joan's apartment opened and a Latina woman with a large gold cross around her neck emerged with a black Labrador. She said hello, and I assumed she was Joan's housekeeper taking the dog out for a walk. The dog was heading for my crotch, but the housekeeper held on tightly to the leash. "Buster, no."

"Thank you," I called out to her. Joan called to me from inside her office and I went in.

"I'm really angry at you." I laughed in recognition of this being my most consistent feeling. But my onslaught continued. "First of all I'm late because of the train and I know you aren't going to give me any extra time. Second, I've told you how much I hate dogs and all along you knew you have a dog and you know that I knew you have a dog, because the fucking dog barks all the time. Then the fucking dog comes out with your housekeeper and tries to sniff my crotch in the waiting room. I need this like a third armpit. Why do I need to pay you to be tortured by your dog?"

There was silence for a few minutes.... I wondered what Joan was feeling. Did she hate me now because I didn't like her dog?

"I'm sorry the dog frightened you. I know you don't like dogs. My housekeeper should not have brought the dog into the waiting room while you were there. She must have assumed no one was there at that time, but you were late. But you seem to be saying that having a dog means I was lying to you—or that it's some kind of betrayal."

I did not answer her right away. At least she realized that I shouldn't be subject to her fucking dog sniffing my crotch. But, was Joan going to make it my problem that I didn't like dogs? A surge of outrage came up.

"Yes, I feel like you were lying to me in a way. You knew all along that you were going to leave me out on the porch with the dogs and you never let on. You acted like you sympathized with me about how cruel my mother was and all along you're probably sitting there thinking, 'Hmm. I wonder how she'll feel when she sees my Labrador? I wonder if she knows I have a dog?'"

"So I was being sadistic like your mother? I don't care if you're scared of dogs either?" she asked.

I remembered walking on McDonald Avenue under the elevated train. I was seven or eight years old. The street was empty and then suddenly a man jumped out from the alley behind the Culver movie theatre with his erect penis sticking out of his pants. I ran home as fast as I could and when I got into the house, my mother was cleaning the kitchen. I stopped in the hallway to catch my breath and then greeted her.

"Hi Mom," I said nonchalantly.

"Take the laundry across the street," she said, pointing to the hamper in the bathroom.

There was a washing machine and dryer in the basement of the apartment house across Webster Avenue and that is where we did our laundry. I did not tell her what happened; I did not tell her I was frightened to go across the street by myself.

I packed up the laundry and walked out the door, looking around for the man. I did not see him as I walked down the steps holding the large bag of laundry. My heart pounded, but I kept walking. Just as I was about to cross over to the apartment house, Mrs. Cohen called to me from the second floor of the apartment building.

"Rose, come up here," she yelled.

I looked up at her leaning out of her window and she gestured with her hand. "Come up here!"

I hurriedly entered the lobby and out of the corner of my eye I noticed the man who was exposing himself across the street.

Now I turned my attention back to Joan.

"I don't think you're sadistic," I said in a hushed tone, "but I think you don't care what I'm afraid of."

"What do you mean?" she asked.

"You got a dog even though you knew I hate dogs." I crossed my arms over my chest. "Not only do you have all these other patients and your family, but you even love a dog."

There was silence for a few minutes. I couldn't see her, but I heard her behind me in her chair, crossing her legs in one direction and then the other and squirming around.

"So, you feel…" she spoke slowly, enunciating each word, "…that if I cared about you, I wouldn't have a dog?"

I hit a nerve talking about her dog. Little bubbles of anxiety floated up.

"Okay, I know that doesn't make sense," I said. "If you want a dog it's your business. You probably had the dog before I was a patient."

I took a deep breath.

"I have no right to expect you not to have a dog just because I don't like dogs," I said. "I just wish you didn't have a dog. That's all."

But then all of a sudden another wave of anger overtook me. The bicycle chain slipped off again.

"I don't understand how you can love a dog? It's an *animal* for God's sake."

There was silence. A spasm in my big toe made me get up and move it around to get the pain to stop. Unable to stop the throbbing, I grabbed my toe and held it, while my face contorted in pain. When the agony receded, the emotional paroxysm faded.

"I want to change the subject," I said. "I went and got a brochure for the Washington Square Training Institute. I've decided I want to start psychoanalytic training when I finish my dissertation. I think that's what I've wanted to do since junior high school and I kept putting it aside because I already spent most of my waking hours thinking about what I feel and what everybody else feels. If I majored in psychology or studied psychoanalysis, I'd never think about anything else.

So I kept choosing things that were far from it—majoring in political science, grad school in sociology. But I'm tired of avoiding it. I want to be a psychoanalyst."

"Well, that's an important decision." Her voice was calm. "We need to talk about it. But our time is up for now."

⇒»×«⇐

I avoided looking at her face when I left her office. First I had a crazy rant about how I hated her dog and then I told her I wanted to be a psychoanalyst. As I walked to the subway, I thought about my mother's rages. I remembered one Saturday morning when I was ten years old. I got out of bed and looked for my mother.

She was lying on the bathroom floor in her *shmata*, pushing and pulling the wooden brush across the white tiles. Her motions got faster and faster.

"Mom?"

She didn't answer; she just kept scrubbing.

"Mom?"

Finally, she yelled at no one in particular, "Why do I deserve this?"

"Mom, come on, why don't you stop?" I implored her.

Ignoring me, she scrubbed faster.

"Ma, please get up. Ma stop, please Ma...."

She scrubbed faster and harder and screamed, "All I do is work and clean for you."

"I'm sorry Mommy. I'll do whatever you want, just get up...."

She got up, mumbling, "You're so selfish."

"I didn't do anything."

"Don't talk back to me!" she barked and slapped me across the face. She held her hand and cried. "See what you did!"

I wanted to hit her; no, I wanted to hold her.

"I'm sorry Ma." I didn't know what I did to cause her yelling. I didn't take out the garbage, I didn't wash the bathtub, I didn't vacuum the bottom of the closet, I didn't dust under the bed. There were so many things that I did wrong that I could have given her a multiple choice test. I knew the answer was "All of the above." She wanted me to read her mind; she wanted me to know what she wanted without having to tell me. I tried, but I *couldn't* read her mind.

After dinner, when the dishes were done and I got into bed, she ironed. I listened to *The Lone Ranger* on the radio. "Hi, ho, Silver, away." I loved the clippity clop of the horse shoes. I could smell the steam from the iron as my mother pressed our clothes. My father was out selling Cutco knives to make extra money. Calm and safe, I inhaled the odor of the steam hitting the cotton. Mom wasn't angry; she wasn't yelling.

Now I was the one yelling.

May 8, 1968

I scowled as I sat in the rocker in the waiting room reading about Robert Kennedy winning the Indiana primary against Gene McCarthy. I thought Kennedy was an opportunist who entered the race late and took advantage of the grief over the assassination of Martin Luther King, Jr. to gain the support of African-American voters.

"Hi, Rose." Joan smiled at me as she came out of one of the doors from her apartment. She wasn't in a session. I imagined she was having a late lunch before seeing a string of patients into the evening. She was wearing a sleeveless white blouse and a blue turquoise necklace that lit up her face.

She opened the door to her office and I walked past her toward the couch. She smelled clean; it wasn't a perfume, but maybe Ivory soap or Pond's cold cream.

I took my shoes off and settled in on the couch.

"I met this guy Tom at my study group," I said, leaving Robert Kennedy aside. "The members are mostly graduate students teaching as adjuncts. We have bagels and lox and talk about books every other Sunday morning. Tom came as a guest of one of the members."

"Oh?" she said, inviting me to tell more.

"He's a Marxist. We had a big argument about Trotsky's role in the revolution. He thought he was going to run rings around me, but I did my undergraduate honors thesis on Trotsky so I surprised him. He's very tall and muscular—he doesn't look like an academic. And he likes to build things—he said he makes bookcases. I'm sure he isn't Jewish. Muscular carpenters named Tom aren't Jewish."

"You just met him," she said, "and it sounds as if you're thinking about marrying him."

"Yeah. I know. I wrote this little note to you over the weekend." I sat up on the couch and reached for the paper in my bag and continued sitting as I read it to her.

> I'm cramped for space. There's not only a three-year-old who lives with me, but my mother lives with me too. We all live together unhappily—the three-year-old and my mother are constantly battling with each other and with me and I don't really have any time or energy left to deal with anyone else.

"So it's your concern about your mother's judgment that's making you size him up as a husband?" Joan asked.

Resistant to telling her the whole story, but unable to hold it in either, I said, "Well, not being Jewish is actually the least of it. He's married."

"It sounds like you didn't want to tell me that," she said quietly.

"No, because it gets worse." The air conditioner rattled. I spoke very quietly, hoping she wouldn't hear. "He's got a child. He came over to my apartment to measure the walls for bookcases. He said he would make me built-ins and he would only charge me for his expenses. So he came over and measured and I ended up making out with him. He said his back hurt so he lay down on my rug and I massaged his lower back. Then I kissed him and soon he was lying on top of me."

I remembered the weight of his body on top of me; the excitement of feeling his erection between my legs.

"I told him I didn't want to have sex with him and he said fine. He just rolled off me and started telling me about his wife and his son. His wife is a nurse—they got married when they were in college and she's supporting him through graduate school. He has nothing to say to her anymore, but he's attached to his little boy and doesn't want to leave him...."

She waited for a few minutes and then broke the silence. "What are you feeling?"

"I'm wondering what you think of me." My stomach was tight in expectation of a blow.

"What do you imagine?"

"I imagine you think I'm doing something wrong and you're wondering why I'm doing it." The tightness passed.

"It sounds like *you* think you're doing something wrong."

"I've always had contempt for women who have affairs with married men and here I am on the brink of doing it myself."

"What was the contempt about?"

"It was a moral judgment about it." *Oh shit, maybe she's had affairs with married men.* "It's wrong to break up some other woman's marriage and cause a child to grow up without her father. On the one hand, that's grandiose because if things were fine, the man wouldn't have an affair. But, on the other hand, I know I wouldn't feel good about myself."

"You seem to think you're doing something wrong and you're wondering why you're doing it."

"Yes, I wonder what I'm doing. Even if I wouldn't be the cause of his marriage breaking up, I'd be the catalyst." My jaws tightened.

"Maybe it's easier to imagine I'm critical of what you're doing than for you to feel the conflict. You're attracted to him and he's exciting, but you feel having an affair with him would be wrong."

"Don't you think it's wrong?" I asked. My eyes narrowed.

"I think," she said, "we each have a sense of what will make us feel good about ourselves and what will make us feel bad about ourselves. It's not the same for everyone. The important thing is for you to be in touch with that for yourself. It's one thing to feel you shouldn't have sex with him because of what I think or your mother will think, and a whole different thing to decide you don't want to have sex with him because you will feel bad about yourself. You will be violating your own sense of right and wrong.... But our time is up, we're going to have to stop."

➤➤➤◀◀◀

I got up and kept thinking about Tom. His arms didn't have any hair on them so the muscles seemed to pop out. Surprising I found that sexy actually because I usually liked hairy men, like Jake, but then I remembered Ken from Hawaii. He didn't have any hair on his arms or his chest either. I'd been aroused by his muscles and the veins under his skin—I liked to trace their path with my finger. There was a blue river on his left hand that split into tributaries about midway between his fingers and his wrist.

June 4, 1968

It was 7:30 p.m. when I arrived at my appointment. The radio announcer was discussing Robert Kennedy's probable victory in California. "Shit," I muttered. Kennedy had won five out of six primaries and seemed a shoo-in for the Democratic nomination, but it had been Eugene McCarthy whose antiwar campaign drove Lyndon Johnson from the field. McCarthy had the guts to oppose the war before Kennedy, yet he was being pushed out. I remembered my first antiwar march down Telegraph Avenue in Berkeley. I had always thought of the police as the people at the Police Athletic League who handed out free tickets to the movies or the roller-skating rink near Prospect Park. Policemen were the people you could turn to if you were lost.

All that had changed on that beautiful October day in 1965. I remembered men with children on their shoulders and women holding babies marching down Telegraph Avenue and police hitting them with clubs. I felt sure one of the cops was going to kill me when he slammed me against a parked car. He was a red-faced man with a smirk on his face as he raised his club. Terrified, I closed my eyes and clenched my teeth in preparation for the blow. But he moved on to the next person.

Now, the dog barked behind the door to Joan's apartment. I wondered if he would knock over the vase filled with white tulips that sat on a small table in the waiting room.

The double doors opened and the lonely "doctor" with the puffy eyes came out of the office with Joan behind her.

"Hi, Rose," Joan said.

I walked over to the couch and settled down. The waistband of my pants felt like one of the girdles my mother wore. She'd huff and puff to pull it up and all the fat was pushed up as if she had a rubber tire around her belly, just above the top of the girdle.

"I'm trying to lose 10 pounds to get back to my pre-college weight. But I can't stand dieting," I said.

I thought about all those dinners at the co-op dorm in college. They were all carbohydrates—potatoes with pasta and some indescribable fatty meat with a gelatinous sauce. Carole and I used to have salami and jack hero sandwiches a few times a week to avoid eating at the co-op. I gained 10 pounds the first semester.

"What makes dieting so hard?"

She cracked open a pistachio nut as she spoke.

Annoyed that she was fooling with the nut, I tried to ignore it.

"I feel so deprived if I can't have good food and enough of it to feel full. Every meal feels like the last supper."

"What do you think that's about?" She chewed on the nut.

I dug my nails into the palm of my hand.

"When we had chicken for dinner, my mother bought a single kosher chicken for the three of us," I said. I moved away from thinking about the pistachios, but I was still thinking about eating. The three of us all liked white meat, so my father ate the breast, and my mother ate the wings, and I was left with the dark meat."

"How do you understand that?" Joan asked.

"Because in the 1950s," I said with annoyance as if everyone knew this, "kosher chickens were fresh killed and sold whole. You couldn't buy extra wings or breasts and it was expensive to buy two chickens."

"Your mother kept a kosher house?" Joan asked.

"Yes, how could you not know that by now?" My voice cracked. She opened another nut.

"You want me to know things even if you don't tell me," she said.

"You're Jewish." My mouth was parched.

"But it's not about my being Jewish, it's about wanting me to know things without you having to tell me."

"Yes, okay, that's true," I confessed.

"Wanting me to know things without you having to tell me is not a problem. Everyone would like the people they care about to read their mind. It's just that you get so disappointed and angry that it's not possible." Her voice was controlled with therapeutic calm.

"Okay. Maybe that's true," I said. But then the flame was ignited again. "In this case, I *did* tell you and you don't remember." I crossed my arms.

She cracked another nut.

"So I forgot something," she said. "What is it that makes that so upsetting?"

I couldn't find a comfortable position on the couch. My lower back ached.

"It's just like my mother. She never remembers the names of my friends. She still thinks I'm getting a degree in psychology. She doesn't care enough to remember anything. It makes me furious."

"It feels as if I'm just like your mother, but I'm not." Her voice softened. "I just forgot something; it doesn't mean I don't care about you."

"Exactly. You're right...," I said. My fists were clenched and my nails dug into the palm of my hand. "But it's hard for me to hold onto because you keep cracking those fucking nuts. Do you know how annoying that is?"

103

"What is it about cracking nuts that's so annoying?" she said mat-ter-of-factly.

"Come on, that's ridiculous," I yelled at her, lifting my head off the pillow. "Isn't it obvious that cracking nuts when someone is talking is rude? Never mind when the person is a patient." My head throbbed. I calmed down enough to speak without shouting. "Look, this is ridic-ulous. You can't turn my annoyance at you cracking nuts during my session into my psychological problem. It's *your* problem. It's rude and inappropriate. What's wrong with you?"

She was silent, but she stopped cracking the nuts. Her silence ad-mitted that cracking nuts was inappropriate, but the muscles in my neck still felt tight.

"But, anyway...," I said, trying to move on, "I had lunch with Lin-da today and I had a BLT on whole wheat toast with mayonnaise. God I love that sandwich."

Joan was quiet. I turned my head from side to side to try to relax my neck.

"In the sixth grade, I was close to Susan Feldman. She introduced me to *American Bandstand* and we spent many afternoons after school dancing together and watching Dick Clark introducing Fabian, Con-nie Francis, Frankie Avalon and Annette Funnicello—the kids from Philadelphia. Susan was Jewish, but unlike my family, they weren't kosher. I loved having lunch there on Saturdays because her mother made the most delicious sandwich I'd ever tasted—bacon, lettuce, and tomato on whole-wheat toast with mayonnaise. Ambrosia. The smell of bacon lingered for hours. I couldn't get enough of it."

Joan was quiet. I tried to ignore her. I imagined bacon crackling in a pan.

"Was it the smell of bacon," she asked, "or the smell of something forbidden by your mother?"

I smiled. "Yes. It was a guilty secret."

"I guess this explains why it's hard for you to diet!" Her eyes widened and she raised her eyebrows for emphasis. "Our time is up for now," she said. I got up from the couch and she surprised me by continuing to talk. "I want you to know that I think you're right. I shouldn't have been eating nuts during your session. I apologize."

⟫⟪

My anger had been thick and black and now it dissipated into the air. My shoulders relaxed. Joan admitted she was wrong, something my mother would never do. I whimpered as I got up from the couch. For the first time I broke the "can't talk after the session is over rule" and looked Joan in the eye and said, "Thank you. That meant a lot to me." But when I walked out of the office into the waiting room, the dog was barking again.

I thought about the huge dogs my upstairs neighbor has. They look similar to the dogs that pull sleds in Alaska and they have leather contraptions over their mouths. They are probably trying to prevent the dog from barking, but I imagined they were to prevent them from biting people. Sometimes when I got on the elevator and my neighbor got on with the two huskies, I felt impelled to smile and talk about the weather while they went right to my crotch and sniffed as if they were looking for algae under the ice. It infuriated me. Why do I have to be subjected to that? I could feel the anger coming back, the loose bicycle chain was slipping off the gears again. Part of me felt self-righteous and justified in my rage. But another part of me loathed my emotional incontinence; it made me feel like my mother.

The Institute

I enrolled at the National Psychological Association for Psychoanalysis (NPAP) at the end of June 1968. I chose it because it provided a more intensive training program than the one at Washington Square Institute and there weren't many psychoanalytic training programs that would accept me without a degree in social work or psychology. NPAP was founded by Theodore Reik, who had a doctorate in psychology and had been analyzed by Freud.

When Reik fled the Nazis and came to New York in 1938, he was denied membership in the New York Psychoanalytic Society because he was not a physician. Although Freud believed medical training diminished people's ability to interpret the unconscious, the New York Psychoanalytic Association was controlled by psychiatrists and refused to train anyone without an MD. In response, Reik created his own institute that welcomed non-MDs—anyone with a master's degree in anything—philosophers, historians, anthropologists, whatever. He also created the Theodore Reik Clinic where patients who could not afford the high fees of most MD psychoanalysts could get treatment.

My first class was Anne Shapiro's pre-practicum course held over the summer for students who had no prior clinical experience. The class was held in Anne's office, which was in a brownstone on East 87th Street. She, her husband, also an analyst, and their daughter lived on the top two floors, and her office was in the basement. When you walked the few steps down from the street to her office, you entered a vibrant waiting room. There were prints of Diego Rivera's murals and handwoven textiles in bright colors—red, orange, yellow. I imagined Anne and her husband and daughter walking through the native market in Coyoacán, tasting the varieties of ceviche and chatting with the dark-skinned women. Anne looked about ten years older than me—Joan's age. She wore peasant blouses and no makeup, giving her a Woodstock-like persona. I imagined her listening to Joan Baez and smoking pot on weekends.

She asked the class to role-play as a way of preparing for our first session with a patient. Alan Barron volunteered to be the patient and I volunteered to be the analyst. Alan had a wry smile and a cracked lower front tooth. He looked like a guy who made pastrami sandwiches at the Second Avenue Deli, but he was a history professor at Princeton. He enrolled at NPAP because he was writing a psychoanalytic biography of the Turkish nationalist Kemal Ataturk. He was not interested in clinical practice; he wanted to write about Ataturk's Oedipal problems.

Alan, the pseudo-patient, sat silently looking at his hands. There was a weight pressing on my chest. I could hear myself breathing. The silence was making me fidget. I didn't know where to look; I didn't want to stare at him.

It seemed as if an hour had passed, but it was only a few minutes when Anne asked the class, "What do you think the patient is feeling?"

"Anxious," Bob Roberts called out. He was an English professor at Kingsboro Community College and wanted to use psychoanalysis in his literary criticism. But he wanted to have a practice too.

Anne turned to me and said, "By staying silent, you are increasing the patient's anxiety. There are times that you want to do that. But it's not a good idea in the first session because you don't know how much anxiety the patient can tolerate. If you stay silent the patient may be overwhelmed and not come back. You might want to say something reassuring: 'It's difficult to sit down and talk to someone you've just met.' That invites the patient to talk about his anxiety."

That seemed so obvious once she said it. I worried that maybe Joan hadn't been doing things right. I turned to Anne and said, "I thought the patient had to begin the session and the analyst was supposed to wait. That's what my analyst does."

To my relief, Anne tossed her long brown hair to one side, smiled, and replied, "Yes, of course. You've been in treatment quite a while and your analyst knows you can tolerate the silence. Also, you have a working alliance with her, but that's something that has to be developed."

But Joan had been silent and waited for me to speak at our first session. She didn't know if I could tolerate the silence or not; we didn't have a working alliance yet. The truth is that I had a hard time tolerating it. It made me furious!

A month into the class, I was sure I wanted Anne Shapiro to be my supervisor once I started seeing patients. She was perfect. In addition to her reassuring way of offering guidance, she mentioned in class once that she and her husband had marched for civil rights and against the war in Vietnam.

My second class was Personality Disorders taught by David Markowitz.

"Borderlines start having a transference on you immediately—sometimes it starts on the phone. From the get-go they are repeating some unconscious relationship. They might start acting out in the initial call—'Oh, I can't make any of those times. Do you have any hours on Friday night or Saturday?'"

The class laughed, but I wondered if I was a borderline. Borderlines have separation problems and a lot of anger. I certainly fit that description. They have trouble feeling ambivalent because their main defense is splitting. Everything is black or white and that creates paranoid tendencies. Borderlines usually have a domineering and controlling mother and a passive father who didn't protect the child from the mother. That certainly sounded like me.

Dr. Markowitz continued, "Borderlines who ask questions on the phone before coming are poor analytic risks."

I couldn't remember if I asked any questions on the phone before starting analysis.

"They have trouble with boundaries—they call you all the time or write letters to the analyst," David Markowitz continued.

I'd written letters to Joan between sessions. I scribbled a note to Alan sitting next to me. "Oh, no, I'm a borderline!" Bob leaned over to read the note and laughed.

When I finished the first stage of my coursework, passed my matriculation exam, and got a referral for my first patient, I asked Anne Shapiro to be my supervisor.

September 24, 1968

As I entered Joan's waiting room, the double doors opened, and the blond "lawyer" emerged. I hadn't seen her in a while because Joan had been on vacation for the month of August. The "lawyer" was pregnant and smiled at me when she came out. I smiled back as if we were agreeing that her work with Joan had borne fruit—as if we had been through something together. After all we'd been seeing each other come and go with tears and smiles for almost two years.

Joan told me to go into her office and she'd be back in a minute. I went into the living room/office and looked around the large room. I didn't want to lie down on the couch and wait for her. I imagined it would feel awkward to be lying down when Joan walked through the door. Also, I was full of nervous energy because I had not seen Joan in such a long time. So, I walked over to the windows and looked at the books on the shelves. There was *Mother* and *Selected Short Stories* by Gorky; she even had a copy of *Dead Souls*. The tales of Chichikov had led me to all those Russian history classes in college. I smiled at the idea that Joan liked Gorky as if that meant she would understand me better.

Jewish Stories by Sholom Aleichem surprised me because Joan seemed so un-Jewish. I fantasized that she read this because of me. But maybe she was reading that with the same eye as she was reading Gorky—just literary interest. Five minutes passed and Joan had not returned so I picked up a book, *In the Shadows* by George Aronstein. I opened the cover and there was a note on the title page: "To Joan: My loving little sister. Love, George." I quickly closed the book and put it back on the shelf. Then I walked over to the couch and sat down in preparation for Joan's return.

"Hi, Rose, sorry I kept you waiting." She walked past the couch to her recliner.

Trying to decide whether I should confess silenced me. I decided I wouldn't be able to talk about anything else if I didn't tell her about it.

"I'm ashamed to tell you, but I looked at your books while I waited for you. I picked up a book and it was written by your brother—it had a note inscribed in it...." I waited for her indignation at my intrusiveness, but she didn't say anything. "I'm sorry."

"What are you sorry about?"

"Well, I shouldn't have looked at the book. I shouldn't have found out your maiden name or that you have a brother who's a writer. I shouldn't know that."

"What makes you feel you shouldn't know that?" Joan asked. Her voice implied, "What's the big deal?"

"It's private. I'm not supposed to know about your life." I wrapped my arms around my chest and pouted.

"You mean you think there's a rule that you're not supposed to know about my life? It's forbidden?" Her tone made it seem silly to worry about.

"Yes, you're my analyst and I'm not supposed to know about you."

"Well, it's true that it's part of the process that we explore your fantasies about me and my life. If you knew all about me that would cut down on the fantasies. But the point is not that you're not supposed to know me."

The muscles in my shoulders relaxed.

"So, I wonder," she asked, "if there might be more to your shame and guilt about it than the reality of the rules of analysis?"

I chuckled. "Once when I searched my parents' bedroom, I found *The Illustrated Sex Manual* and I felt guilty that I had been looking in places that were private and I felt embarrassed that I found out something sexual about them. The cover was torn in places and certain pages were dog-eared so it was clear that it was used...."

"Yes?" she said.

I knew she wanted me to continue, but my shame had a firm hold on me.

"So I knew," I said slowly as if to put off having to tell her, "they used the book for ideas about sexual positions and stuff. It wasn't for me to know."

"Was it also exciting?"

I held my breath for what seemed like a long time, but finally let it out. "Yes, it was exciting. I used to sit on their bed and read it. I remember looking at the pictures of oral sex and thinking, 'I can't believe my mother would do that.' If I heard the lock in the door I'd quickly replace it and run into the kitchen before they opened the door." I hesitated before I continued. "So I guess picking up the book while I waited for you felt like I snooped on you the way I used to with my parents. It was a guilty pleasure. And then when I found the book written by your brother with the inscription, it was hitting pay dirt. I found out something I wasn't supposed to know—something private. I was afraid you would catch me so I put the book back and sat on the couch so you would think I'd been patiently sitting there the whole time you were gone."

"It's interesting that you had so much evidence of your mother being sexual and yet you continued to feel that she wasn't. I wonder what that was about?"

I covered my mouth with my hand and started thinking about the "lawyer."

"What are you feeling?"

"I thought about the lawyer being pregnant."

"What lawyer?" She sounded confused.

I laughed because I realized this was all in my head. "Oh, I've always had a fantasy that patient with the blond hair is a lawyer."

"What about that?" There was a smile in her voice.

"Well, I think she's a WASP and she's extremely attractive and well-dressed so I decided she must come from a wealthy family and be a graduate of Harvard Law School. I imagine she works for a fancy law firm and her husband's a fancy lawyer too."

"You have quite an active imagination. . . ." She chuckled. "So what do you think this is about?"

"I guess it's about feeling that she's better than I am and that you like her more because I'm a poor *shlep* from Brooklyn and she's an upper-class WASP from Greenwich or somewhere."

"And you think I prefer WASPs? What gave you that idea?"

"You didn't do anything to give me that idea. I saw your daughter a few sessions ago. She was taking the dog out for a walk. I thought how lucky she was to have you as a mother. She seemed so content. I imagined the way you smile at her and hug her and tell her how pretty she is and how much you love her. You must have read *The Little Prince* to her when she was younger and told her she was your special rose."

"Did your mother ever read to you?" Her voice was gentle—as if she already knew the answer.

"No, I don't think so," I tried to imagine my mother sitting on a chair with me sitting on her lap. I couldn't. My mother used to straighten up my bed though when I was sick. I used to love that. She'd have me get out of bed and she'd straighten up the sheet and the com-forter and fluff up the pillow. I used to think it was surprising I didn't become a hypochondriac because I have such pleasant associations with being sick. It's the only time she was comforting. She never held me or kissed me, but at least she tried to make me comfortable." I imagined Joan reading to her children every night before they went to bed and straightening up the bed when they were sick. I decided to take a risk and ask her a personal question. I took a deep breath.

"Is your daughter your only child or do you have other children?"

"What do you imagine?" she asked.

My jaw tightened. "I'll tell you what I imagine, but I can't stand it when you don't answer the question first. I feel you're playing with me; it feels sadistic. I hate it."

"Okay, yes, she's my only child. What did you imagine?"

"I imagined," I said, still trying to keep the cork in the bottle, "you had a picture perfect household—a husband and a son and daughter."

"You mean you thought I had a picture-perfect life just like the 'lawyer'?" Joan said.

"Yes, I see. First I idealize and then I'm jealous."

"Well, my life is not picture perfect," she said. "I'm divorced and I have a daughter."

She was giving me more information than I even asked for. And she's divorced! I realized that must be why she moved her practice from the clinic to her house. She wanted to be home for her daughter.

"Thank you for telling me," I sighed.

"You're welcome," she said softly, "but our time is up. We're going to have to stop."

⇢⟫⟨⟨⇠

I chuckled to myself as I opened the door from the office to the waiting room. I had been walking around with the fantasy about "the lawyer" for two years. Maybe she wasn't so perfect. Maybe she was adopted and her parents abandoned her; that's why she's so happy to be pregnant. Maybe she went to Brooklyn College and works in a bank. As I entered the waiting room, one of the doors from Joan's apartment opened and her daughter came out with the black lab on a leash. I had seen her with the dog before; she looked about 16 years old. Her long brown hair flopped on her face as the dog pulled her. She wasn't strong enough, or didn't have the inclination, to keep the dog from investigating my crotch. I smiled to make her think I didn't mind and held the door open for her. She thanked me and we both waited silently for the elevator. I felt privy, once again, to something I wasn't supposed to see. But this time I didn't feel guilty.

October 22, 1968

Walking to the subway, I was thinking about Anne Shapiro. I loved her warmth and admired her empathic stance and wanted her as my supervisor. But I imagined Joan feeling jealous of my relationship with Anne. After all, Anne wasn't my analyst, she was my teacher, so she was free to share her opinions and personal stories the way I had always yearned for from Joan. I was hesitant to talk about my feelings about Anne in my sessions with Joan because I liked seeing Anne and I was afraid Joan might feel jealous.

I thought about my aunts—Hannah and Gus. When I was 13 my parents planned a trip to Florida for their twenty-fifth anniversary. They went off for a week. I spent a week at my Aunt Hannah's house in Valley Stream, Long Island. Hannah had the timid look of someone who had been emotionally unnourished, but she had beautiful green eyes that made your muscles relax when you looked into them. They glistened like a National Geographic photo of a glacier-fed lake somewhere in the Rockies. She told family stories that seemed to come from the same natural source. In contrast to my mother and Gus, Hannah made no effort to be attractive. She knitted her clothes and everyone would say how beautiful they were, but they were made in unflattering styles and never quite fit right.

Hannah was not social like her sisters. Although my mother didn't chat with our non-Jewish neighbors, she and Gus had wide social cir-

117

cles. Aunt Hannah, on the other hand, talked to the Italian neighbors, but didn't seem to have any friends. Gus was always bragging about something, but Hannah was humble and self-effacing.

I enjoyed being away from the elevated train on McDonald Avenue that made our ground floor apartment shake every time a train stopped at Eighteenth Avenue. Aunt Hannah and Uncle Morris had lived next door to us on Webster Avenue when I was very little, but they were able to buy a pastel pre-fabricated house on a former potato farm in Valley Stream. My grandmother moved with them and perhaps she gave them some money for the down payment. She had died a few years before my visit. Uncle Morris worked as a truck driver for a mattress company and got up to make his deliveries long before the sun came up. He was gone before I got up in the morning and had breakfast with Aunt Hannah. I loved listening to Hannah's stories; I remember every detail about family members I never met. It was during that week that Hannah told me a family secret that helped me understand my mother in a way I never had before.

"My mother, your Grandmother Nettie, was the oldest daughter of four children. The man your mother and I knew as our grandfather, wasn't really Nettie's father. In Russia," Hannah said, "my grandmother's parents made a match for her—though she was deeply in love with another man."

"You mean they *made* her marry someone she didn't love?" I gasped.

Hannah explained, "Yes, that's what they used to do. Marriage wasn't based on love; it was based on the desire of the families to be connected for financial reasons. When your grandma was an infant, her father was in a mysterious accident and drowned in the river."

"Do you think your grandmother *killed* him?"

"I don't know, I've often wondered that."

I allowed myself to wonder too. "I bet it was raining torrents and great-grandfather's horse was running in the rain and your grandmother hid behind a bush and threw a rock at the horse and the horse whinnied and went back on its hind legs in pain and great-grandfather fell off his cart and broke his neck."

"Could be," she snickered.

Imagining was fun. "Or maybe it was a beautiful afternoon and he got off his cart and was looking out at the lake and your grandmother's lover came and pushed him in the water and he drowned."

"No, I don't think he would have done that," Hannah said. "My grandfather, or step-grandfather, was a wonderful man. She's the one who could have done it, not him." Hannah rubbed the back of her neck. She said, "Actually, I think the wheel came off his cart and he was thrown from it and broke his neck."

My mother had told me that when she and Aunt Gus went to their grandmother's house when their mother was working, she made them eat bread and butter in such copious amounts that neither of them ever wanted to smell or eat butter for the rest of their lives. That made me wonder. "Maybe she loosened the screw on the wheel of the cart?"

Hannah smirked as if to say her grandmother *was* indeed capable of such a thing.

"So what happened after he died?" I asked.

"My grandmother," Hannah said, "soon married Harry and the two of them came to the United States with her little daughter Nettie—my mother. Her stepfather loved Nettie, but her own mother hated her." Hannah had a pained look as if she had a gas pain. "My grandmother had three children with Harry after they came to New York and she clearly preferred them to my mother. Indeed, when my grandmother died she left all the money she made on the stock market to the three children from the second marriage. If my mother had any doubts that her mother didn't love her, it was clarified in her will. Remember Uncle Sol had a car dealership? He bought it with the money he inherited and," she added bitterly, "my mother got nothing."

When I returned from my glorious week with Aunt Hannah, Gus and Joe were at our house as they usually were on Sunday night to watch Ed Sullivan with us. Uncle Joe was not handsome and he walked like a large penguin, but he was a lawyer—the only professional in the family. He had an abundance of hair everywhere—his ear drums, the back of his hands, even the inside of his arms. But only a small rim of hair encircled his scalp.

Joe was sitting in the chair he commandeered whenever he was visiting. It was the special chair close to the television that I coveted. Uncle Joe told me to sit someplace else as soon as he arrived. He bullied me, but tip-toed around Gus.

I was talking about what fun I had at Aunt Hannah's house. Rather suddenly Aunt Gus screamed. It was chilling, like the echo of a whale.

"You know why you had such a good time? It's because you have no friends."

I looked at my mother—hoping to see horror in her face. But there was none. Most wild animals get fierce when their babies are endangered, but my mother was not one of them. My mother and father sat silently looking at the floor.

Aunt Gus continued, "If you were normal, you wouldn't *want* to spend so much time with Aunt Hannah."

I was defenseless against her. My parents watched. They never mentioned it afterward. I might have forgiven them, because I understood they were too frightened to confront Gus directly, if only they had pulled me aside afterwards and reassured me that Aunt Gus's attack was not really about something being wrong with me, but about her jealousy of my relationship with Hannah. But neither of them ever said that.

Now, when Joan came out of her office to greet me, I was shaken out of my trance. I followed her into the office and headed for the couch. I was about to take my shoes off when Joan asked me to sit up because she needed to speak to me. My heart throbbed—something was terribly wrong. She had never started the session by talking to me; she always waited for me to say something. She hadn't seemed herself in the last few weeks. Three weeks before she had forgotten Linda's name and the week before I could tell she wasn't really listening when I told her a dream. Her nail polish was chipped and there were still specks of it left on two of her fingers. No time for the nail salon either. Her usually sparkling blue eyes looked tired and dimmed by the dark bags under them.

I had been angry at her for almost two years because she never started the session and it was always incumbent on me to say something. Now that she was finally speaking first, I dreaded that she was sick or dying.

I grabbed a pillow and propped myself up on the couch. When I settled in there was a moment of silence. I could hear a slight wispy sound as I listened to my breathing. I dug my nails into my palms, trying to ready myself for the bad news I knew was coming.

I hummed silently: "I love you true and blue and like glue."

Then Joan looked at me somberly and began to tell me what I had feared.

"I have breast cancer and need to have an operation, so I'm going to have to stop seeing patients for a while."

I winced as the salt in my tears ran into the cold sore on my lip. She spoke softly and simply, like a mother reassuring a young child. "I'm going to be all right. But I won't be able to work for a while." I thought about her breasts, so small and flat. I wondered how she found the tumor. Did she touch her breasts in the shower and feel a lump? That's the way my father's cousin Bertha found hers. Or was she in bed with a lover who felt a little bump?

I pictured myself putting my arms around her, and laying my head on her lap as I had longed to do for so long. I imagined her stroking my hair and saying: "I'm going to be back. Don't worry. I'm only going to be gone a little while and then I'll be back." I wanted to hold on to her the way a child holds onto a parent who's going out the door. Flooded with regret for all the times I'd expressed anger at her and the loving moments I'd let pass silently, I wanted to yell, "I'm sorry, I'll be good. Please don't leave me."

"I love you," I finally said. "You know that, don't you? I get angry at you all the time because I want so much from you. Too much. More than you can possibly give or anyone can. I don't want you to be in pain. I'd do anything for you. I want you to be okay."

"I know," she whispered.

Joan folded her hands in her lap before she spoke; I thought she was trying not to weep. Her voice was stilted and she spoke slowly.

"The doctor says I will have to have chemo and radiation after the operation, but I will survive it. I can't work because I will be sick from the chemo and then very tired from the radiation."

I wanted to ask her a million questions: Did you get a second opinion? Are you going to Sloane Kettering? What stage is it? Is there lymph node involvement? Are you having a mastectomy? How long will you be gone? But somehow, even then, I knew those questions would not feel good to her. I understood that asking sick people about their medical details was an expression of anxiety that was like pouring water into a cup that was already full. I wanted to soothe and reassure her.

"Can I visit you?" I whispered.

"Let's talk about it," she said.

I closed my eyes.

"How would it feel for you to visit me?"

Her face looked puffy as if she had been crying a lot. For the first time I noticed the brown spots on her cheeks like the skin of an apricot. I'd never felt she was vulnerable before; a wave of sadness washed over me.

"I think it would feel good," I said. Our relationship had been all about my wanting Joan to love me; to care about me in a way my mother never did. There had been no room for me to give her anything—to take care of her. She had done all the giving.

"I want to give *you* something."

"Did your mother allow you to give to her?" she said quietly.

Taking a tissue from the dispenser on the table, I wiped my face, but it was too late, my blouse was already damp from the run-off.

"Ironically," I said, "I think she was constantly angry and complaining that no one took care of her, but she couldn't take it in. If I put my arms around her when she seemed sad, she never put her arms around me. It was always one way. She made constant demands, but she never asked for a hug."

"Don't you know telling me how you feel about me is giving me something?"

»»»«««

My head was throbbing when I got up from the couch, but I noticed the tall vase was empty. Joan loved white flowers; she always had a bouquet sitting on her coffee table. Sometimes there were showy double peonies. Other times she had mop head hydrangeas as big as your head, elegant lace caps, or dainty roses mixed with voluptuous tulips. Now I realized the vase had been empty for weeks. I had been oblivious to her pain. My mind turned to her surgery. I contorted my face, imagining a doctor with a mask and gloves raising the scalpel to cut into her. A wave of nausea rose up from my stomach to my throat.

Leaving Joan's building, the sunlight was jarring. The porter was hosing the sidewalk, so I took a detour to avoid the spray. But a toddler on a tricycle, going too fast for his mother to catch him, drove right through the puddle and showered me with brown water. I had the impulse to yell at him, but his mother's horror at the state of my slacks and her immediate apology, drained the anger. Just ahead of me was a couple engrossed in an argument.

"Why do you always have to confront my mother?" the woman asked. She looked like a tube of toothpaste that's been squeezed while the top is on. "Why can't you just let her say whatever she wants and ignore her?"

"That's impossible," he said. "She's the one who confronts me. She looks straight at me and says: 'Do you really think that shirt matches those pants?' How can I ignore that?"

I speeded up to get past them so I didn't hear her response. I didn't need to—I could finish the conversation.

A little while later I sat on a park bench. I watched a young mother rocking her daughter on the baby swing. The girl giggled with delight every time she was suspended in the air and the mother sang as she pushed:

How do you like to go up in a swing,
Up in the air so blue?
Oh, I do think it the pleasantest thing
Ever a child can do!

I remembered roller skating in the schoolyard and hitting my head on the edge of a cement step. Dizzy and shaky, I managed to remove my skates and walk home. When I got there, Aunt Gus and Uncle Joe were visiting. Lightheaded, I sat on the couch wishing my mother would notice that something was wrong with me. But she didn't. She kept talking to Gus and Joe.

Now, I got up and started walking toward the subway. Unlike that little girl on the swing, I wasn't sure if there was going to be someone to catch me.

PART II

MEETING STEPHEN

January 6, 1969

Dear Joan:

It's been more than two months since you told me you were sick and I'm anxious to know how you are feeling. I think about you every day, hoping you aren't in pain and that you are being well cared for. It's like a subway under a tall building; there's a constant rumble underneath everything I do.

I've seen Tom a few times and I realize he's a really selfish guy. Although he has a flexible teaching schedule and his wife works many more hours as a nurse, he doesn't take any responsibility for child care or cooking. He's always free to hang out with me because he ignores his wife. He treats her as if she's hired help and jokes about her. I'm still attracted to him, but I don't really like him. I'm over him.

I'm taking two courses this semester at NPAP and they're fascinating. The two teachers have completely different approaches. Scheinman is rather orthodox and focuses on the Oedipal complex, while Malkoff is much more focused on early mother-infant interaction and other pre-Oedipal issues. It's like the blind man looking at the elephant. Each one of them tends to see the aspects of the patient that reflect their own theoretical point of view.

I think the analyst's personality has a lot to do with their theoretical point of view also. The orthodox guy seems rigid in his response to student questions. Of course, he doesn't appreciate my questions in class. Part of what strikes me is how crucial the chemistry between the patient and analyst is. I don't think I could have worked with that guy the way I've worked with you. Part of what has been so transformational for me has been your willingness to admit your part in things that happen between us. It drains the anger and allows my loving feelings to flow more freely.

I had a dream that the world is going to end and Linda decides to take a pill and get it over with, but I don't, because it's not 100 percent definite. In the end the world doesn't end and she's dead. I think it's about my feelings about you. Part of me feels like I'm never going to see you again and the other part of me feels hopeful that you will come back to me.

Love,
Rose

Stephen

Stephen came to my Sunday study group meeting on January 19, 1969. He had gold-rimmed glasses and wore an old sport jacket with pockets ripped and stretched by years of cold hands snuggling in them. He looked like a Parisian intellectual and, indeed, he had spent two years in Paris researching his dissertation on the right-wing anti-Dreyfusards at the end of the nineteenth century. In the end, he had given up on getting a PhD because there were hopelessly few university openings in history, and he was now working for Mayor John Lindsay as a lobbyist for the city.

The first time Stephen came to the group we all piled into his car and went to the movies and out for Chinese food afterward. After he dropped off the others, he drove me home. Stopping at my front door, he looked straight ahead as if he were still driving.

"I'm going to visit my mother in Florida for a week, but maybe we can have dinner when I get back," he said.

"I'd really like that. Have a good trip." His shyness and vulnerability made me believe him. He wasn't going to be like so many other guys who told me they would call and never did.

Then he turned and smiled at me. His shy hazel eyes looked at my face, but seemed afraid to fully take me in.

When I walked into my building a flood of excitement washed over me—instead of taking the elevator I decided to jog up the five flights of stairs to my apartment. I imagined telling Joan about him, but on the third flight realized I couldn't. Joan wasn't seeing patients yet.

Two weeks passed and he didn't call. I had to bear the disappointment without Joan as well. I thought he was going to be "the one." I moped around feeling stupid for having been excited about him. Maybe it was a good thing I hadn't been able to tell her how great he was because it was turning out that he was just another jerk like all the other ones I'd dated. Like the hypocritical rabbi or the Jewish airline captain I met through Black Book who wanted to have his foreskin put back. Finally, after almost three weeks he called.

"Hi, I'm sorry. I stayed longer than I thought. My mother is in a bad way. She's really depressed and the dog is dying. I just had to stay. My office was great about giving me the extra time."

I sighed with relief.

On our first date we went to the movies. It was after nine o'clock when we got out and we were both starving. He said, "Have you ever been to that Indian restaurant on your block?"

I hadn't, so off we went. But we were the only people in the restaurant. Four waiters hovered over us.

Out of their earshot, he asked, "Do you like Indian food?"

Chewing on the parantha, I admitted, "I'm embarrassed to tell you I've never had it before. I love this bread though."

"I've never had it either. Next time we'll go someplace French, okay?

When we went back to my apartment, Stephen stayed for a couple of hours. When he left, he kissed me lightly on the neck, his tongue sliding up to my cheek and then finding its way to the lobe of my ear. He explored my ear for a minute and then put his hand on my cheek to turn my mouth to his. First he kissed me lightly on the mouth and then his tongue circled my lips until he kissed me slowly and deeply.

After what seemed an endless amount of time, he whispered, "Can I come back tomorrow?"

"Sure," I whispered in his ear, "I'll make brunch." After that weekend Stephen had to go back to Albany to work with the legislators for the week. So we had an early dinner at a Chinese restaurant and he parked in front so he could leave from there. When we embraced and kissed goodbye and I watched him get into the car. I cried for ten blocks until I reached my apartment, like a little girl whose parents had abandoned her. I had been so lonely without Joan and so filled up by Stephen. Now they were both gone.

February 4, 1969

Dear Joan:

I hope you're feeling stronger and will be able to come back to work soon. I miss you and can't wait to talk to you about everything that's going on.

I'm absorbed by the course I'm taking on dreams with Sheinman. The unconscious use of metaphors in the way the patient describes the dream is absolutely mind blowing—i.e. "banged up" or "trying to find a way out." Of course, I understood this on some level from the way we always work on dreams, but I'd never articulated the process in these terms.

I've been thinking a lot about getting fired from the Yeshiva and feeling guilty. I was subversive and by engaging the students in it, I set them up for disappointment. I gave them a taste of the outside world, but they were not going to be able to partake of it. It wasn't right.

Sometimes I feel that way about you. You and I have these intense disagreements and I get angry at you and we work it out and afterward I love you even more. But that doesn't happen in the real world. Out there I get disappointed and angry and tell the other person, but I can't work it out with them. The process is truncated; the relationship just ends. I want to find people who can go down that path with me and work through the hurt and anger when it inevitably arises.

I've met someone I really care about—Stephen. He's in my history study group and he's different than anyone I've ever met before. I spent the weekend with him. It happened so fast. When he left I felt bereft the way I used to feel when our sessions ended. I can't wait to see you.

Love,

Rose

February 21, 1969

I rang the buzzer and entered Joan's waiting room thinking about what it would be like to see her again. I hadn't seen her in almost four months when she called to say she was able to work again and we could resume my treatment. I wondered if Joan would be wearing a wig and whether she would look bulimic from all the vomiting caused by the chemotherapy. I brought an orchid in bloom, a Phalaenopsis, with long arching stems studded with white flowers. Lost in admiring the centers of the flowers that looked like little red insects with black dots, I was startled when the door to the office opened and the Lilliputian walked out. Joan was behind her wearing loose-fitting black cotton pants and a long, white sleeveless top that reached the middle of her thighs. I realized she was wearing a wig—it was wavier and a little darker than her natural hair. She looked tired, but her eyes sparkled. "Hello, Rose." She smiled broadly. "I'm so happy to see you."

"Oh God, not as much as I am to see you," I said. Laughing, I handed her the orchid. She held the ceramic pot out in front of her to have a more complete view of the arcs of the stems; two droplets slowly worked their way down her cheekbone. She made her way into her office and put the orchid between the two ferns that had permanent places on the bookcase under the windows. Then, before sitting in her chair, she took a few steps back and admired the way the orchid seemed to take up the green from the ferns, adding splashes of white

137

and red. As I walked over to the couch to lie down, I noticed a large bouquet of red and yellow gerberas on the coffee table near the tissues and I assumed another patient must have brought them—maybe the Lilliputian. For so long my feelings had been blunt instruments; I was relieved that it didn't bother me that another patient loved her too. I wanted Joan to have as much love as possible, not just mine.

I lay down on the couch, sighing with pleasure because I finally believed that I mattered to Joan. The tension in my back seeped away as if I had immersed myself in a warm bubble bath. "I'm so glad to be here. I've missed you so much."

"I'm glad to be here too." She chuckled.

"How can I just talk about myself without referring to what you've been going through? I know you're not going to talk about it, but it feels weird to ignore it."

"I understand that it's awkward. Is there something particular you want to ask me?"

"No, I just don't want you to think that I'm not thinking about you and what you've been through," I said.

"I know that and I appreciate it," she said softly. "But I'm back and I'm okay. So let's talk about what's going on with you."

"I've been seeing a lot of Stephen. He's pretty much living at my apartment. But he has to go to Albany every Sunday night because he's a lobbyist for the city, and he comes back on Friday night."

"Yes?" she said with a smile in her voice.

"I hate it. Every Sunday night I have a mini-depression. Luckily I'm working on my dissertation proposal and I have to prepare for my classes at Brooklyn College so it takes my mind off him."

"Why don't you tell me about Stephen?" she asked.

"He's different than any man I've ever known. He has trouble saying what he feels, but I know he really cares about me. I'm more sure of it than I've ever been with anyone."

"And how do you feel about him?" she asked.

"I am so drawn to him I want to be with him every minute. It's funny though, he isn't interested in psychoanalysis at all. A few years ago when he was living in D.C., he was in a deteriorating relationship and had a few sessions with an orthodox Freudian who didn't talk. But his father died rather suddenly and he moved back to New York. He doesn't want to go into treatment again because he hated the analyst's silence. It turned him off to the whole process."

"Do you think he needs it?"

"Yes! He doesn't have a particularly good relationship with his mother or sister who live in Florida and he hated his grandmother. Can you imagine, his parents had him share a bedroom with his grandmother, while his sister had her own room!

"That makes me worry about his feelings about women. Also, he has done all the research for his dissertation, but hasn't written it. That makes me worry about whether he has a problem completing things."

"It sounds like you feel you have a future with him," she said.

"Yes, but if Mayor Lindsay loses the next election, Stephen could be out of a job. So I really want him to finish his dissertation."

"Well, we are going to have to stop for now."

I got up from the couch and she smiled at me.

"I'm so glad you're back," I said.

"And I'm so happy to be back and see you again," she said grinning.

⸎

139

I walked down Broadway thinking about Joan. I let out a big sigh of relief, and a woman walking close by turned and looked at me quizzically. I smiled. Then my thoughts turned to Stephen. He had studied in France as both an undergraduate and graduate student and loved croissants—especially Zabar's chocolate-filled croissants. Since it was a Friday, I decided to walk to 80th Street before I headed downtown, and buy some croissants and bagels for us to have over the weekend.

March 12, 1969

I sat in Joan's waiting room thinking about seeing my first referral from the Theodore Reik Consultation Center—Mary Elizabeth Donovan. The description in the referral form said that she had recently returned from the Peace Corps. She was assigned a ten-dollar fee because she had no savings and was employed in a menial job earning minimum wage.

I had a few Italian friends growing up, but no Irish. I attended P.S. 134 and most of the Irish kids in the neighborhood attended St. Rose of Lima. We didn't interact very much—except during snowstorms when the Irish boys threw snowballs at the public school kids and yelled, "The Jews killed Christ!" We Jewish kids had no idea who St. Rose of Lima was. We thought the school was named after the bean, not the city in Peru, so we pronounced it that way. I did not learn that St. Rose of Lima was the first saint to be canonized in the New World, until college.

I wondered how uncomfortable I might feel treating an Irish Catholic woman. I imagined that Mary Elizabeth wore her hair just the way those parochial school girls did in the 1950's—you could see where the rollers had been placed in their long hair. And instead of a flip, their long hair was neatly tucked under just as it reached the chin.

I was shaken out of my reverie when Joan came out of her office and held the door open for me.

"Well... I'm feeling very anxious about seeing my first patient," I said as I took off my shoes. "I'm so glad you're back. I have no clinical experience—I just get thrown in the ring. What if someone commits suicide because of me?"

"Anne will supervise you so you won't be completely on your own and you can talk about what's going on with me as well so it's unlikely that you'll drive anyone to suicide unless they were already set on it," she said. "There's always a first patient ... In fact," she added in a smiling voice, "you were one of my first private patients."

I breathed deeply. "It's funny, I always wished I was your first patient, but I hesitated to ask."

She sounded surprised. "Really, what made you hesitant?"

"I didn't want you to feel insulted. If I thought I was your first patient, you might think I was saying I thought you were inexperienced."

"Do you think that?" she asked.

"Well, I know you are a social worker and had training and experience before your analytic training," I said.

"Yes, I had internships when I was in social work school and worked in a therapy clinic before my analytic training," she said.

"But I think you've evolved. In the beginning of our work together, you had the attitude of 'the patient is always wrong.' I used to think it was a good thing you didn't own a restaurant."

She laughed. "That's terrible: 'The patient is always wrong.' What do you mean?"

"You used to take the position that I had to accept whatever you did or it was my problem. That felt like my mother. There was the time you were cracking nuts in the session. That's a ridiculous thing to do in a therapy session, you have to admit. How could it be my problem that I didn't like it? Especially pistachio nuts!"

142

"Yes, you know I was in analysis with Bob Malkoff and I realize now he felt that he could do whatever he wanted and then analyze the patient's reaction as if it was their transference issue. I guess that's what the pistachio nuts episode was about."

I could taste the salt on my lips. "That means so much to me. I think it's so good when I can understand your reactions in a context that's about you." I hesitated. "So did you leave Malkoff?"

"Well, I terminated with him and started to get interested in self-psychology," she said. "It's an entirely different approach."

"I read Kohut's book *Analysis of the Self*," I said. " He's the rage now, but I don't really get the concept of 'mirroring.' In my NPAP classes the people who are self-psychologists seem to be the dumbest ones in the program. They just repeat what the patient says. It's stupid."

"Well, I think there's a lot of misunderstanding about what 'mirroring' means," Joan said. "It isn't just repeating back the other person's words. It's mirroring what the other person is feeling. That's a lot harder and more healing."

"I just remembered I had a dream last night. I was sitting outside a restaurant eating with someone. A low-flying plane comes over us and there's a small plane attached to it, being carried. They crash in front of us on the left. Everyone is yelling and running. I see Bob Stolorow. He's shook up, but not hurt. Then it's a quarter to four and I call the woman who is my supervisor to confirm our appointment and she seems surprised. She forgot and says, 'Oh, I'm all confused because of the crash.'"

"What made you think of the dream just now?"

"Stolorow's a self-psychologist like Kohut and I know you worked with Stolorow for a while."

"What was the feeling in the dream?"

143

"It was frightening. Everyone was hysterical."

"What comes to mind," she asked, "about a big plane with a small plane under it being carried?"

Whenever she repeated things they sounded so obvious.

"A mother with a baby, maybe?" I crossed my arms over my chest.

"You're starting analytic training and I teach at the institute. Do you think I might be the big plane and you're the little one?"

"The teacher in my Psychoanalysis of Dreams class said all dreams are about the relationship with the analyst. I had been skeptical when he said that, but this is clearly a transference dream."

"Yes. What about the planes crashing?"

"Well they crash because they're connected?"

"Yes, a big one and a little one are connected."

She seemed to see straight into the marrow of the dream, but I didn't get it.

"What comes to mind about a big one and a little one?" she asked.

The image of a woman holding a child's hand washed over me. "You're a big one and I'm a little one," I said. "I'm just starting to be an analyst and you've been doing this a long time." My arms relaxed.

"And what about Bob Stolorow?" she asked.

"Well, he's famous—a big plane. Maybe you're a little plane in relation to him."

"Or maybe he's a stand-in for me," she said.

"He survives the crash!" I said chortling.

"Yes," she laughed, "I survived the crash."

"Maybe the crash is your illness."

"Yes. What about it being a quarter to four?"

"I have my Thursday session with you," I chuckled, "at a quarter to four."

"Yes. Can you say what you're feeling?"

144

"The supervisor forgets the appointment with me. I'm not on her mind."

"Yes," she said, "but how did that make you *feel* in the dream?"

"Horrible. I didn't matter to him. But I couldn't be angry at him … After all there had been this crash." I shrugged and raised my eyebrows.

"Maybe you were afraid that I'd forgotten you when I was ill."

"Yes," I said. My chest heaved. "I was not on your radar and it made me feel lonely."

She didn't speak, but let out an audible noise that let me know she was sympathetic to my feeling lonely without her.

"What are you feeling?" she asked.

"Guilty."

"About what?"

"That you were dealing with breast cancer and I wanted you to be thinking about me. It makes me feel selfish and stupid."

"I don't think it's selfish or stupid. I think it's perfectly understandable."

"I love you, you know." I sobbed. "It's been so hard not seeing you."

"I know." Her voice was tender like a mother speaking to a young child who has managed to occupy herself while her mother was on the phone. "I know it's been hard."

She didn't try to make me feel bad about myself for needing her. Her empathy decanted my mixed up feelings about her. The sediment had all sunk to the bottom. What was left was clear and rich; I loved her.

"I think my mother made me feel that something was wrong with me for being dependent on her," I said.

"Yes, her message was that you shouldn't feel bad when she put you on the porch," she said softly. "But that's ridiculous. It made her angry that you needed her and you couldn't stop needing her. And when needs are not met it makes you feel needy. It's a vicious cycle. But our time is up for now."

⟫⟪

I got up slowly, feeling dizzy. I admired the way Joan had deconstructed the dream. My feelings had bubbled up in my dream—a geyser that only erupts at night. I needed Joan even if she was sick. But she understood that. It was as if we had uncovered an old mine shaft filled with rotted wood beams. I kept falling into it over the years and getting bruised and battered. I'd fallen in again, but this time Joan was there and she offered her arm and helped me climb out. Then we cleared away the debris together and let the light in. It was still there, but it was no longer treacherous. I smiled at John when I got on the elevator and was grateful that he smiled back without saying a word.

My First Patient

Within two months of meeting, Stephen stayed with me on weekends; he went to Albany almost every Sunday through Friday for work. But he still had his cockroach-ridden studio apartment on West 71st Street across the street from where a prostitute was murdered by one of her Johns. Just being there conjured up memories of *Looking for Mr. Goodbar.* I would never sleep there—it took so much out of me to even walk in and help him pack his books. It made me itch.

When a two-bedroom apartment became available in my building, I convinced Stephen to rent it with me. I planned to use the second bedroom as an office because it had an attached bathroom. It was perfect because he was in Albany during the week and I put up a folding screen of bright orange Marimekko fabric so that patients would not see our living room when they walked into the office. There was no waiting room, so I decided I would answer the door and usher the patient into the second bedroom/office.

Mary Elizabeth was my first patient in the home office. When I opened the door, sure enough, she looked like one of the Irish girls who went to St. Rose of Lima. She had porcelain white skin and wore something close to a Catholic School uniform—a wool tartan plaid skirt, starched cotton blouse with a round collar buttoned up to the top, and a blue jacket. I imagined her walking to school with heavy books and pamphlets about the lives of the saints.

Before she sat down across from me, she neatly folded her black wool coat. Then she sat bolt straight, her coat on her lap and legs perfectly parallel during the whole session.

The referring therapist told me Mary Elizabeth had been in Sierra Leone and had returned to the United States suffering from a major depression. She was living alone and, despite her college degree and teaching experience, was working at a minimum wage job.

She seemed cool and a little distant at first, but within minutes she was crying intensely as she explained how depressed she felt.

"I feel like I've just had a terrible accident," she said, "and I'm stuck on a block of ice … The wounds are all exposed and I'm in agony, but the idea of peeling me off is even worse, absolutely terrifying."

Riveted to my seat, I sat silently. She continued to sob, taking a white cotton handkerchief out of her purse. Holding my breath, I waited for her to continue.

"I came home from Sierra Leone a few months ago," she said. "I'd gone there after the coup in 1967 when the All People's Congress won the election. I wanted to be part of the democratic change, but of course all that soon went down the drain with the military coup. I was living in a small village called Saiama in the savannah. But I came home to visit about a year ago and when I went back to Africa I just couldn't function. First I went back to my village, but I couldn't get out of bed in the morning; I couldn't eat. My friend Nelly, who I'd gone through training with, came from Freetown and took me to stay with her in the city. But I just got worse and worse. Finally, she insisted I come back to the States. I lived with my parents for a while, but I couldn't stand it. Now I'm living in the basement of a house in Brooklyn and working at Maimonides hospital."

"What kind of work are you doing at the hospital?" I asked.

"I'm folding sheets and cleaning bedpans."

She was scarcely functioning. "It sounds as if something about your visit home touched off your depression. Do you know what it was?"

"I think it was my mother," she said. "I always felt she was jealous of me. She resented anything I had in my life that she never had. After my time working in the rice fields and living in a hut, I thought she would finally stop feeling angry at me and be proud of my accomplishments and independence. But instead, she said: 'You get to see the world and I'm stuck here in bed.' She has terrible arthritis. It made me want to kill myself. I want to stay in bed and pull the covers over my head. Every step I take is like walking through molasses. It takes so much energy to move my left foot forward and then my right foot."

I waited for her to continue, but I didn't want the silence to go on too long.

"You sound depressed," I said gently.

"Yes, I know that. I'm barely getting by," she said, crying hard. "That's why my friend Betty said I should see you. She really likes her therapist and she told Betty you were really smart and good."

Frightened by the depth of her depression, I started thinking about my mother's friend Eleanor who had committed suicide.

"Have you thought of the possibility of taking medication?" I asked.

Her posture got more rigid and her face was taut.

"No, I would never do that...." She spoke in an icy voice.

I knew that was a mistake. Frightened by the depth of her depression I had suggested medication too quickly.

After a few moments, her posture and face softened. She whispered. "I don't want medication. I'm afraid I would lose my mind." She stared at the floor.

My mouth dropped. I was glad she wasn't looking at me.

149

"Okay, but if you don't want to take medication," I said haltingly, "you really need to come more than once a week. I know you aren't earning much money so I'll be happy to adjust my fee based on the number of sessions you want to come."

She folded her arms around herself and started to sway like an Orthodox Jew davening. Finally, her words came out a child's voice.

"Don't make me love you," she said.

My eyes widened. She looked puzzled.

"I have no idea what that means," she said. She spoke as if she were talking about a third person in the room with us. "It came from nowhere."

She fell silent and her demeanor changed again. She pulled her legs up on the chair like a little girl and hugged herself.

"If I breathe, you won't have the air to breathe," she whispered trying to limit her intake of air.

Frightened by the drastic change in her persona, I dug my nails into my palms. I was unsure of what was happening to her. I bit the inside of my cheek.

"What do you mean?" I asked.

"I don't know ... ," she whispered. "I just feel it intensely."

The hair on my arm stood up. I checked the clock in hopes that the session was over.

"We're going to have to stop in a couple of minutes so why don't we talk about setting up your appointments."

"How often do you think I should come?" she asked.

Unsure about whether I would be able to tolerate the intensity of her depression, I also feared she might hurt herself. The concern for her overtook the fear.

"I think it would be a good idea for you to come three times a week." I held my breath to see if she recoiled. A big smile came to her little girl's face. Her voice gained strength.

"Yes, I want to do that. I definitely want that."

I exhaled with relief.

"Good," I said. "Then I'll see you on Wednesday at six."

⟫⟪

Mary Elizabeth got up from the chair and carefully put on her coat. Her deliberateness was in stark contrast to the confusion and terror she experienced in the session. She seemed to live in a haunted house with rooms walled off from each other. She found herself in one and had no idea how she got there and before she could get her bearings she was in another room and equally baffled. She was letting me in to her inner life. I was in one of those rooms with her—and I didn't understand how I'd gotten there or where a secret door might open leading to another room. Frightened of the inexplicable feelings that seemed to overtake her, the demons lurking in those rooms, I pondered what might be in there—physical abuse, incest, rape?

It was like the beginning of a supernatural horror story and I wasn't an exorcist—just an inexperienced analyst-in-training.

151

April 3, 1969

I sat in Joan's waiting room thinking about my mother's friend Eleanor. My mother never would have known her if she had not gone to work as a part-time bookkeeper in a Sunoco station on Coney Island Avenue when I was eight. My mother had been a full-charge bookkeeper for a garment manufacturer in downtown Brooklyn before she got married. I sometimes wondered if she regretted giving that up; she always became animated when talking about her friends from work. They went to dances together and she met my father at one of them.

My mother could add a list of numbers a page long in her head, but she had not worked for ten years so she was starting as an assistant bookkeeper. Her boss was Eleanor Condon, a broad-shouldered woman who was much taller than my mother, with reddish-brown hair and smiling brown eyes. She wore a gold cross around her neck and her son went to Catholic school. My mother and Eleanor sat side-by-side in a cramped office with a view of four gas pumps; the dirty windows made it always seem like a cloudy day.

My mother didn't interact with non-Jews. When the vegetable cart came to Webster Avenue and the children ran to greet the old, tired horse, my mother stood on line and talked to Mrs. Moskowitz from the apartment building across the street or Mrs. Samuels who was our landlord. I watched in horror as she nodded, but never spoke, to Mrs.

Rizzetti or Mrs. Poggi, although I played stoop ball with their sons and Gerard Rizzetti was a regular visitor to our house.

My mother never invited non-Jews to our house, so I was proud of her when she invited Eleanor and her family for dinner. Eleanor and Pete and their son Ronnie came on a Friday night. I smiled remembering Pete, who was the tallest man I had ever seen—a former college basketball player. He was the kind of man who is so tall that he develops bad posture from trying not to bump his head and having to lean over to talk to people. Ronnie was tall as well—he was thirteen, four years younger than me at the time, but a foot taller. He had curly red hair and crystal blue eyes.

"What a beautiful candelabra!" Eleanor said to my mother when she walked in.

"It's for *Shabbas*," my mother said, clasping her hands together, "Friday night is special for Jews. We light candles."

Eleanor took it in stride, but I remember how uncomfortable Pete and Ronnie looked. It was as if they had gone to Africa and discovered a tribal ritual.

My father's friends, the Keffords, were never invited to dinner. My father visited Mary and Tom Kefford, an elderly childless couple, alone or with me. They had emigrated from England to the United States in 1952. Tom retired after the death of King George VI, for whom he had been a royal footman. My father had sold them an oil burner, but afterwards he became devoted to them and visited them weekly to "check their tank," make sure they had enough groceries, and have a chat. My mother refused to join him and registered her contempt openly. "Why do you bother with those goyim!" she yelled at my father whenever he left the house to visit to Keffords.

I thought about the times I visited them with my father—just the two of us. The Keffords' windows had lace curtains rather than the drapes that we had and their heavy furniture looked old and used. At the time I didn't understand that these were antiques. I thought it meant they couldn't afford to have new furniture like ours. Mary Kefford, a razor-thin woman with gray hair, always served tea and cookies that she called "biscuits"; she poured the tea out of a china teapot and put the spoons on cloth napkins.

One Sunday afternoon, when I was in the fifth grade, Tom Kefford asked me what I was learning in school.

"We read *The New York Times* in Mr. Zamore's class every Thursday and then discuss current events. He even taught us how to fold the newspaper when we read it," I said excitedly.

"What have you learned about?" he said in his pronounced English accent.

"We're learning about the mob," I said.

"And what is the mob?" he asked with a chuckle, leaning forward in his stuffed chair.

"It's the Mafia, a group of criminals that came from Italy."

"Really? What have you found out about them?" he asked with a big smile.

"Well, the FBI uses undercover agents to act like they belong and they gather information to use it against them," I said.

Out of the corner of my eye I could see my father smiling at the interchange. My words came faster. "One of their bosses, Frank Costello, got convicted on tax evasion," I told him, "and went to prison."

Tom Kefford tilted his head and turned to look at my father with raised eyebrows.

I beamed and nodded at Mr. Kefford as if to say, "Yes, I really know about this."

Visiting the Keffords was much more fun than visiting my paternal grandmother in Brighton Beach. There was no conversation at my grandmother's house, just an awkward silence. But my father came alive when he talked to Tom—he delighted at his dry humor and never tired of Tom's stories about the royal family.

My paternal grandfather died when my father was five. The man my grandmother married out of desperation had his own children and never treated my father or my uncle Bob the same way he treated his own children. But Mr. Kefford treated my father as the son he never had; when he died he left my father a small sum of money in his will to thank him for all the years he cared for them.

Then my thoughts returned to Eleanor.

When Joan came out to greet me I was jolted as if I had been dreaming and she shook me.

"For some reason," I said, "I just thought about my mother's friend Eleanor. She was my mother's only non-Jewish friend.

"To my surprise and pleasure, my mother loved Eleanor. Her relationship with her seemed different from her relationship with any of her Jewish friends. Eleanor told my mother about her problems and my mother seemed to really care," I said tearfully. "After a few years, my mother left the Sunoco station and got a job at a meat packing company in Bedford Stuyvesant. But she and Eleanor remained friends—they talked on the phone regularly." I wiped my moist cheeks with my hand. "My mother's other relationships were about canasta or mahjong, not about sharing feelings and problems."

"I guess that isn't surprising," Joan said. "It must have been perilous for her to share her feelings with her sisters."

"Yes, especially with Gus. But my mother didn't share her feelings with Eleanor either. It was mostly Eleanor sharing her feelings and my mother listening. When I was in college and her son, Ronnie, was still in high school, he was in an automobile accident that ended his future basketball career. After several operations, one of his legs was left shorter than the other." I rubbed my forehead and shook my head. "After that, he was seriously depressed and developed a drug problem. Sometimes when I was home, I overheard my mother speaking on the phone with Eleanor. She wasn't judgmental with her, but all the empathy she could muster was a set a platitudes:

'He'll be all right.'

'Don't worry so much about him.'

'It's not your fault.'

'What can you do?'

'He'll snap out of it.'"

"What do you make of that?" Joan asked, shifting in her chair.

I remembered when Pete called my mother. Just before Christmas in 1964, Eleanor swallowed a fistful of pills and died. My mother was distraught. She sat at the kitchen table sobbing, "Oh Eleanor, how could you do such a thing?" She was moaning, "Eleanor, how could you do that?" Even when my maternal grandmother died, I had never seen my mother experience such paroxysms of grief. I remembered holding her as she rocked back and forth in agony.

"Maybe she couldn't bear Eleanor's pain," I said.

"Yes," Joan said.

"She wanted her to stop feeling it. But I wanted my mother to bear it. I wanted her to be able to say: 'Yes, it's horrible. I'm so sorry.' Maybe she was being genuine; she just didn't know how to console her."

"It's not surprising.... She never was able to console you," Joan said matter-of-factly.

"It wasn't just because she didn't love me." I frowned. "She didn't have it to give."

"Yes... But why do you think you're talking about your mother's friend Eleanor now?

I laughed.

"That's a good question," I said. "I think it's because of my new patient, Mary Elizabeth."

"And how is that related to your new patient?" Joan asked.

"She reminds me of Eleanor maybe just because she's Catholic and really depressed. I think I'm afraid she's going to kill herself and it will be my fault."

"Why would it be your fault?"

"Because I couldn't stop her." I bit the inside of my cheek and my face was contorted.

"You don't have the power to stop her if she's set on it. But what makes you feel she could kill herself?" Joan asked.

"She never tried or anything, but there's something so dark about the way she talks... I feel frightened for her." My eyes squinted. "I want to protect her."

"Unfortunately, our time is up for now."

⟫⟪

I looked at Joan and smiled. She had put on weight since she returned to work and looked rested. I walked out feeling a jumble of emotions. Leaving her building, I started thinking about the Picasso exhibit that Stephen and I had seen at the Met. The paintings could have been displayed in so many different ways. I finally understood how the curator affects our viewing of the images by organizing the paintings according to a theme and spotlighting a line of inquiry for the museum visitor who might otherwise stroll through the gallery haphazardly. I was struck by the parallel between the curator and the analyst. Of course, the curator has the advantage of knowing all the material before organizing it while the analyst builds connections as she goes. Joan did not know there would be a connection between Eleanor and

Mary Elizabeth, but she had a gift for juxtaposing things that seem superficially unrelated.

Supervision

After seeing Mary Elizabeth for a week, I had my first supervisory session with Anne. When I got to her office and sat down in the waiting room, my chair faced a Frida Kahlo self-portrait. It wasn't one of those with the monkey on her shoulder and that black unibrow looking like a winged creature. And it wasn't the famous one with the thorn necklace and the hummingbird. She painted so many self-portraits they don't even have names—just dates. This one was much softer. I had never seen it anywhere else. Her face and neck were elongated and she was wearing a sexy low-cut blouse. I smiled to myself wondering what it meant that my analyst had a Georgia O'Keeffe poster and my supervisor had a Frida Kahlo.

I couldn't imagine that Anne identified with Frida's disability or her anger and depression—especially since this self-portrait was so soft and sensual. I decided her appreciation for Frida had more to do with her love of Mexico and her left-wing politics.

Joan's appreciation of Georgia O'Keeffe was easier to understand because she loved flowers. But perhaps more importantly O'Keeffe seemed to see sexuality everywhere—in rocks, flowers, even rams' heads. I smiled to myself thinking that Joan was able to discern sexual undercurrents in my associations and dreams that were not obvious to me.

"Hi, Rose," Anne opened the door to her office and greeted me. She was wearing a yellow and green dress and large silver hoop earrings.

She pointed to the chair that was facing her desk and I settled into it as she walked around her desk to sit down. She pushed her long brown hair off her face and looked at me.

"Well, it's nice to see you," she said with lively eyes. "So you met your first patient," she said.

"Yes," I said soberly.

"Well?" she said, lifting her eyebrows.

"Her name is Mary Elizabeth and she's coming three times a week."

"Really, that's great, but how did that happen?" she asked.

"She's really depressed," I said. "I'm kind of afraid to tell you this because it's probably a mistake. She was so eerily depressed when she came to the first appointment that I started having an anxiety attack. I was afraid she'd kill herself. So I suggested she take medication."

"Why were you afraid to tell me that?" She played with her silver hoops.

"I thought I shouldn't have suggested medication right away." I slouched.

"I don't think you have to worry about it," she said, stroking her chin. "How did she respond?"

"She refused. She said she was afraid she would lose her mind."

"So it's not a problem that you suggested medication right away. You sensed it was a severe depression right away. And she confirmed it. She told you she's afraid of becoming psychotic if she takes psychotropic medication," Anne said, nodding her head.

"Yes, she looks like this strait-laced Catholic school girl on the outside, but she started to tell me about her dreams right away. She brings in dreams almost every session and her associations are primal."

"What do you mean?" Anne asked. Her eyes narrowed.

"They're always long and complex and they scare me."

"What about them scares you?" she asked.

"She is so in touch with her unconscious. It just pours out of her." My eyes widened.

"Yes? What about that?" she asked, tilting her head slightly.

"I think she reminds me of an Irish woman my mother used to work with. Her name was Eleanor Condon and she and my mother became friends."

"So why would that scare you?" Anne asked gently.

"She was depressed for years and committed suicide when I was in college."

"So that's why you're afraid Mary Elizabeth might kill herself?"

"Yes."

"Do you know if she's ever attempted suicide?"

"She said she hasn't, but she's thought about it."

"Did you ask her what she thought about exactly?"

"Yes, she said she thought about jumping off a bridge."

"Was it any particular bridge?" Anne asked.

"No, I don't think so."

"Well, if it gets specific about where she would jump, then you should be concerned. But as long as it's just a vague fantasy, I don't think you need to worry."

"Oh..." I took a deep breath.

"She's not your mother's friend Eleanor. And she's coming to see you three times a week."

"Yes." I nodded.

"She's obviously attached to you already and that's going to help her." She smiled.

Mary Elizabeth

"I'm still amazed that you allow me to come three times a week. I want to use the couch," Mary Elizabeth said.

"Can you tell me more about it?" I asked.

All my analyst-in-training friends regularly complained that they could not get their patients to come three times a week or use the couch. But my experience with Mary Elizabeth was the opposite. She felt that I was doing her a favor by *allowing* her to come three times a week and use the couch!

She got up from the chair across from me and walked to the couch. It wasn't an analytic couch, it had arms, but she took off her shoes and carefully put her feet up. She fastidiously straightened her skirt, pulling it down to cover her knees. My chair was just behind the head of the couch, a little to the left so I could see the tears streaming down her cheek.

I heard Stephen in the hall and hoped she didn't. On occasion, when Stephen was home while I was seeing Mary Elizabeth, he moved the screen and walked down the hall to the bathroom. She probably didn't notice, but I did. I could hear his steps in the hallway. He didn't like having to be so careful in his own house and I didn't want to think about him while I listened to a patient. My jaw tensed.

"I want to do this," Mary Elizabeth said. I relaxed, thinking she probably didn't hear him. "I want to get all of this stuff out of me. I feel like my mother, father and I were in separate rowboats on a lake and each of them had an oar out to keep my boat from touching theirs—it was a triangle...."

I imagined three boats floating on Prospect Park Lake with the oars extended so they never touched. She was moving closer to me as she was telling me about her parents keeping her at a distance. I thought this was good sign; I couldn't wait to tell Anne.

"So you felt you had to stay away from them or they would push you away?" I asked. I heard the toilet flush and grimaced.

"Yes, exactly. That's why it's so strange you let me come here. It was part of the deal with them. You could be with them, but don't touch and don't be dependent."

I understood her need to keep her distance for fear the other person did not want her to get too close. I had imagined that Joan would put her oars out if I got too angry at her or if I needed her too much.

Mary Elizabeth was hugging herself and making guttural sounds. I had no idea what was overtaking her, but it was sinister.

"Can you tell me what you're feeling?" I asked gently.

"I feel frightened," she whispered. Her body stiffened.

"Of what?"

"That you're going to stick me with something."

Jolted, it was as if an electric shock had gone through me.

"Stick you with something?" I asked, bewildered.

"Yes, a pin or something. Over here." She pointed to her hip.

I tried to give her space to see what came into her mind.

"I don't know what it's about...." she whispered.

My right eye twitched.

"I had a dream I want to tell you," she said. "I was in a frenzy of cleaning. I was stripping beds and doing machines full of wash. I felt in control and had everything in order. I was alone and happy. Then other people came. I couldn't stick to my plan of cleaning up. I was very angry with my friend Betty and decided I would leave. She was talking very authoritatively to someone and I walked away and it was a beautiful vista of countryside—like Africa. As I kept walking, I was walking toward a window and climbed out onto a ledge hugging the wall of the building and ducked into another window. Someone was selling ice cream and the bowls were wok size, piled high with ice cream. But they were actually piles of washed underwear. I was very disappointed. It was all still wet—nothing hung up."

"Did anything happen yesterday that's related to the dream?" I had no idea what the dream was about. But that's the question you're always supposed to ask first.

"I called my father about my insurance policy. I want to cash it in. My father loved ice cream so maybe that's him in the dream. I hadn't spoken to him in a year and he acted like no time had passed. I wonder if the dream was about preparing to see him. Cleaning and stripping beds is like wanting to have everything under control. I woke up tired. In the dream I wanted to remove myself from Betty's orbit. She was very authoritarian."

"Like your mother?"

"Yes, I think Betty is often a proxy for my mother in my dreams. I wanted to separate myself from her."

"What comes to mind about leaving your mother?" I asked.

"It reminds me of another dream. I was with Peter. He was another Peace Corps volunteer who used to visit me in the village and one night I almost had sex with him. I kept saying no and he kept insisting that we both had bodies and needs. In the dream I was with him and it was very intense. He wanted to have intercourse and I didn't want to, but I had these strong feelings and it was up to me. My whole body was overcome by this desire to grab him; the feeling was growing and growing. Then the two of us were on the ledge of a crater and he bent over and was trying to loosen a boulder. I was afraid he'd fall and then I was trying to hold him, but I was afraid of falling off the edge. Then it turned into a small room with a white wicker couch. The sexual excitement was so intense it awakened me. It was a current running through my whole body, but I wasn't wet. I didn't masturbate."

"In the dream or in reality?" I asked, rubbing my eyes.

"Both. My sexual organs didn't react, but the rest of my body did. It's a 'hold me, hug me' thing with me, a little girl thing."

"Have you ever had intercourse?" I asked. My temples tensed.

"No," she shook her head.

"You said Peter kept insisting you both had bodies and needs. What about that?"

"There's something I hate about sex, but I don't even know what it is. When a woman has sex with a married man they call it 'adultery.' What a strange thing to call it! Is that what it means to be an adult? And is the woman committing adultery or only the married man? Isn't *he* the one who's committing adultery?"

"What comes to mind about that?" I asked.

"My father comes to mind, but I don't know why. He was an adult ..." She got off the couch to get her coat, which was folded on the chair. Then she went back to the couch, lay down, and carefully pulled her coat over her.

"It's about sex. I failed at sex. Life would be so much easier for me if I wasn't a sexual being."

What's making her think of adultery now? And what's the connection to her father, I wondered. What does it mean to *fail* at sex? But I didn't want to cut off her associative flow with all those questions. So I decided to ask her something simple yet open ended.

"What about that?" I asked.

"I've denied my body all my life. I simply did not have one. The only thing that existed was my head. So I lived there. In a completely made up world that was unknown to my conscious self. My ability to deny... to simply erase... elements of the concrete world takes my breath away. The problem of sex never came up until that happened with Peter because I had no body. I had a clothes rack. As long as the clothes were hung correctly on the rack, there was no problem. I think that's how Mom treated her body as well."

"How so?" I asked.

"She didn't want to have a body. After all, she just kept having babies and miscarriages and suffering. My dad didn't want me to have a body either. He could only be comfortable with me if I didn't have a body."

I wondered what it meant that her father didn't want her to have a body. Did he feel he couldn't control himself if she had a body? Feeling queasiness in my stomach, I was relieved when I looked at the clock and realized the session was over.

"Unfortunately, our time is up for now."

➤➤➤◄◄◄

Mary Elizabeth got up to leave. She put on her shoes on and fixed her skirt. I could see the white dots of talcum powder in her shoe as she wiggled her foot into it. She was so careful and controlled on the outside, but her inner world was a pond teeming with life. Her unconscious was just below the surface.

As I watched her walk out the door I thought about her fear of being stuck with a pin. What could that be about? Was her mother psychotic? Did she purposely stick her baby with pins? Or was it a memory of having her diaper hastily changed and being accidentally stuck with a diaper pin?

July 26, 1969

Sitting in Joan's waiting room reading the *Times*, I was outraged that Ted Kennedy got away with murder. Two months suspended sentence for killing someone! He was cheating on his wife as well. I thought he should get two months just for that!

Then my thoughts turned to Stephen. He wanted to go to France. He had spent his junior year in Strasbourg and then two years working on his dissertation in Paris on a fellowship. But he had been poor and lonely there. He couldn't afford to go to good restaurants or drink decent wine. Now he wanted to go back with me and do it differently. He had been planning a trip since March, but since then things had changed. Mayor Lindsay's polls were tanking and it looked like he was going to lose the election and Stephen would be out of a job.

Joan opened the door from her apartment and gave me a warm smile. She opened the double doors to the office and sat down in her chair. I walked over to the couch and lay down.

"I'm worried about Stephen, he's probably going to lose his job soon and he still has his heart set on going to France," I said.

I thought about when my father lost his job because the Hunter Coal Company went out of business. It wasn't his fault, but my mother had so much anxiety about paying the rent that she wasn't sympathetic to his feelings about it.

"What makes you think Stephen's going to lose his job?" Joan asked.

"It's all stuff that's not Lindsay's fault, but it doesn't matter. Forty-two people died in the blizzard in February and he gets blamed for that. The people in the boroughs hate him. Between the garbage strike, the police and fireman slowdowns, and the rising crime rate, he's in big trouble."

"Yes," she said.

"Then in June," I continued, "he lost to Marchi in the Republican primary... Stephen says he's not going to win in November."

"Oy," she said.

"Lindsay's going to lose and Stephen will lose his job," I explained.

"Okay, that's lousy. But that's months away, why are you so upset about it today?" she asked.

"We're supposed to go to France on vacation next month and Stephen could be out of work at the end of the year. I think we should cancel the trip and he refuses."

"Do you think he's ever going to get another job?" she asked.

"It won't be so easy. The next mayor won't hire him and who knows how long it will take to find another job," I said.

"But do you think he will find one eventually?"

"Well, of course, he will," I agreed reluctantly. "But when I was a kid my father lost his job and it took him a few months to find another one. My mother was afraid they would lose their apartment if they couldn't pay the rent."

"Did your mother work then?" she asked.

"She had a part-time job at the Sunoco station, but she couldn't support us on her salary."

"But Stephen isn't your father. And you're not in the same situation as your mother. You have your fellowship and now a full-time instructor's salary—and you're seeing patients," she said.

"True," I agreed reluctantly.

"If he loses his job, you won't be evicted. But you won't have three weeks to go to France when he gets a new job, will you?"

"Okay," I nodded. "I see the point. But there's also the issue of my father."

"What do you mean?" she asked.

"He's got congestive heart failure and he keeps getting pneumonia."

"So are you hesitant to go away when your father might get pneumonia again?"

"Yeah, or he might die while I am away," I said through sobs.

"I understand your concern, but he could go on for a long time like this. It's hard to time when it's going to happen," she said.

"Yes, if we don't go and he's fine, Stephen will be furious at me."

"Well, it's something he's looked forward to for a long time, right?"

"Yes."

"Well we are going to have to stop for now."

Parlez-Vous Francais

Stephen spoke French and I couldn't speak a word. Even though I had two years of French in junior high and four years in high school, I couldn't utter a complete sentence. I could understand some words on road signs like *"Arrête"* and a few things on a menu—*"cochon,"* *"saumon,"* or *"poulet"*—but that was about it.

He had planned the trip for months and made reservations at restaurants and hotels. Feeling completely taken care of, I loved the food and the wine and the countryside. But our differences kept surfacing. Before we left, he obsessed over Bourgeois, a two-star Michelin restaurant in Priay, a tiny town on the fringe of Burgundy. But there were no hotels there, so we stayed in Bourg-en-Bresse and drove 16 miles for dinner.

Excited about the dinner, we arrived early to walk around the town. We found the restaurant quickly and looked at the menu posted outside. I decided to order frogs legs and Stephen said he wanted the famous Bresse chicken. We took a walk down the unpaved street and when we came back for dinner, Madame greeted us at the door, and we walked through the kitchen to get to our table. We walked past an old woman scaling fish and a young girl snapping off the ends of thin string beans. When we were seated, Madame told Stephen, in French, that *omble chevalier* and *poulet de Bresse* were the specials of the evening, not listed on the menu, but they had to be ordered for two. Stephen translated for me.

"She just wants to get rid of her surplus fish and chicken for the day," I said.

Stephen's eyes opened wide. He was aghast, speechless at my reaction.

"We came all this way," he said when he recovered, "to this special restaurant. I've planned it for months. Everything is fresh here; it's a two-star for Christ sake. What's wrong with you?" His eyes blazed.

"You may love everything French, but I don't want some fish I never heard of and who wants chicken poached in a pig's bladder. Ecch!" I thought of my mother's expression if I told her I ate chicken cooked inside a pig's bladder. I imagined the look of nausea on her face, the disgust in her eyes. I folded my arms across my chest.

Stephen leaned toward me and put his red face close to mine. He was trying not to yell at me. "If you insist on having frogs legs, which is the most mundane thing you could order, that will make it impossible for me to get either of the specials. What's wrong with you?"

"Don't you see, she's just manipulating us because we're Americans," I said, paying no attention to the tables of French people surrounding us happily eating either *omble chevalier* or *poulet de Bresse.* "I want frogs' legs please," I said staring at him.

Stephen ordered *ecrivesse a la nage*—one of the only items, other than frogs' legs, for one person.

We sat silently waiting for our dinner. Stephen looked everywhere in the room except at me. His right eye was twitching.

By the time Madame arrived with our food I worried that I had made a mistake. In front of Stephen she put down the large bowl of water, filled with tiny shrimp in their shells with their heads still on. I knew he hated to eat anything that involved using his hands—he only ate lobster if it was out of the shell. It was as if he ordered it to spite me. He grit his teeth. Frightened now that I had destroyed something between us over something as stupid as frogs' legs, my temples pounded.

As quietly as he could, trying not to scream, he whispered, "I hate this. I can't eat it." We sat silently until I finished my frogs' legs and then he asked for the check, refusing Madame's offer of dessert. He didn't say a word for a long time as we drove back to Bourg-en-Bresse. About halfway back he started yelling.

"You are so fucking crazy that you think everyone is trying to rip you off," he shouted. He gripped the wheel so tightly, I was afraid he would drive off the road. "You ruined something I have planned and looked forward to for two years. I will never forgive you for this. You're acting like your crazy mother!"

Frightened that he would be right never to forgive me, I sat frozen. My paranoia had ruined something that really mattered to him.

"I'm sorry," I said as we got out of the car. "You're right, I'm afraid of being ripped off and I just don't believe anyone."

"You really have to get over this," he said. He was only a year older than me and a few inches taller, but I felt like a child being yelled at by my father. "You ruined something that I'd been looking forward to for so long. How could you do that?" he asked.

"I'm sorry. I really am," I pleaded. "I understand that was crazy. Please forgive me, I'm really sorry."

He didn't respond. He just got undressed, brushed his teeth and got into bed.

The next night we had dinner in a three-star Michelin restaurant —Troisgros. It wasn't in a tiny town like Priay, but in a small city, Roanne. We parked at the railroad station and walked across the street to the restaurant.

"No craziness about them trying to manipulate us into ordering anything, right?" he said, tilting his head.

"No, I promise."

Stephen ordered the lamb special and I ordered what was cheapest on the menu.

After dinner, the waiter rolled a cheese cart to our table. Stephen pointed to three cheeses and the waiter dutifully cut tranches and arranged them on a small plate.

"Madame?" the waiter said turning to me.

"No thank you," I said waiving my hands in case he didn't understand English.

He nodded and rolled the cart to the next table.

Stephen cut a piece of cheese, carefully put it on a piece of baguette and handed it to me.

"Taste it," he said, "it's a goat cheese."

"What?" I blurted. I didn't know they made cheese from goat's milk.

"Really, taste it, it's wonderful," he said.

"Okay, thank you," I said relenting.

"This one is Tomme de Chevre Aydius, it has the texture of gruyere, but a grassy sweetness."

"Mmm, I like it," I admitted.

"Now try this Roquefort. It's the champagne of cheese," he said carefully putting a bit on my plate.

The waiter was back again with another cart. This one had three levels filled with raspberry tarts, chocolate truffles, strawberries with heavenly whipped cream, cassis and apricot sorbet, custard-filled pastries and dozens of other delicacies.

I was in shock. I sat silent with my mouth open.

"This isn't Brooklyn. You can have whatever you want," Stephen said.

"It's over the top. I can't do it," I said.

"Okay, if you insist," he said. "But I'm not going to share it with you. This is why we came here. You need to get over it."

When it came time for dessert, I ordered a mundane chocolate mousse and Stephen ordered *le grand dessert*, choosing five or six items from the cart. I sat staring at his plate piled with dark chocolate truffles, fresh raspberries, cassis sorbet, peach ice cream, and miniature pastries. Then we got the check.

"Do you expect me to split the bill?" I asked.

"Oh no, are you going to start in again?"

"What do you mean?" I asked with a shrug.

"You know what I mean. You're doing the poor girl from Brooklyn routine again and ruining everything."

We walked back to the hotel without speaking. When we got to our room we undressed silently and got into bed. It was becoming a frightening routine. I was trying to be conciliatory despite being angry about splitting the bill, but he would have none of it. I turned over.

I woke up in the morning full of self-loathing and fear that I could lose Stephen if I continued acting this way. I lay in bed watching him sleep and in a little while he sensed it and opened his eyes but looked at the ceiling. I stroked his cheek hoping he would not push me away.

"I'm so sorry. I know what I did last night was crazy and paranoid." He turned to me and kissed me lightly on my nose.

"You can take a girl out of Brooklyn, but you can't take the Brooklyn out of the girl." His eyes were red and puffy.

"Yes." I smiled with relief; he wasn't going to leave me.

September 2, 1969

It was my first appointment after Joan's vacation and my trip to France. I sat in the waiting room reading a *Times* story about Salvador Allende being elected Chile's first socialist president. But I was distracted by all the things I wanted to tell Joan. There was good news—Stephen found a new job at a public relations firm that represented the government of Jamaica. But there was bad news as well—we had some major arguments while we were away. I squeezed my eyes shut thinking about dinner in Priay where all of my anger had come up again like acid reflux. Then there was my father's congestive heart failure and the endless trips to the emergency room.

"Hi, Rose!" Joan said with welcoming eyes when she emerged from the double doors of her office.

I headed for the couch and let out a deep breath as if I'd been holding it in for a month.

"Oh my God, so much has happened. I feel like I haven't seen you in a year!"

"Okay, so tell me what's been happening," she said with a grin.

"First of all, my father's been in and out of the ER so many times that I feel like I know the receptionist."

"Why does he keep going to the ER?" she asked.

"His heart is getting worse. It's congestive heart failure. He gets out of the hospital for a week and then he can't breathe and he has to go back."

"I'm sorry. That sounds terrible," she said.

"I'm getting used to it. It's not so bad. I want to talk about Stephen."

"Yes, how was your trip to France?" Joan asked.

"Well, first of all, I'm really glad we went because he got another job and it would have been terrible if we had cancelled the trip."

"That's good," she said.

"But," I continued, "the trip was really a mixed bag. On the one hand, France is beautiful and the food is unbelievable. But we have different attitudes about spending money on extravagant dinners."

"Oh, how are you different?" she asked.

"Well, he orders from the top of the menu and I order from the bottom."

"And?" Her tone sounded like she raised her eyebrows.

"We split the check. We always split everything evenly. And when he insists on ordering the specials and the grand dessert, I get furious at him."

"You don't think it's fair to split the check because he is eating more expensively?" she asked.

"Yes, he says we went to France to eat at these great restaurants and he's not going to scrimp," I explained.

"He has a point, doesn't he?"

"Yes, but he always orders the specials and they always cost more than the regular menu," I protested.

"Well," she said, "I guess you could either decide to stop splitting the check or stop ordering from the bottom."

I'd been struck by lightning. It was so simple. "What is wrong with me? I'm so crazy."

"I don't think you're crazy. But ... ," she said hesitatingly, "you can get stuck on certain things and lose perspective."

"I like sharing our money. We split the rent and I use the second bedroom as an office, but he pays half the rent."

"So it's not such a big deal if he gets the specials?" she said with a smile in her voice.

"It shouldn't be. I don't want to start figuring out who ate what," I said.

"So?"

"So why don't I just order what I want and stop being angry at him for ordering what he wants?" I asked myself.

"Your mother's mantra was you can't have things just because you want them. But she never helped you distinguish between what you could have and what you couldn't have. Some things you want are perfectly attainable. You can have them—like dessert at a three-star restaurant. Not allowing yourself to have what you want makes you angry at Stephen for being perfectly comfortable having what he wants if it's attainable."

"Yes..." I nodded.

"Well, our time is up for now."

⟫⟪

Euphoric walking to the subway, a great weight had been lifted. I couldn't wait to get home and tell Stephen what Joan said. I imagined he was going to laugh and say, "Of course, that's why you get angry at me! I know that!"

I decided to get off at 79th Street and go to Zabar's so I could buy him some chocolate croissants.

Hearing the door open, Stephen greeted me with a kiss, taking the bag. I heard Walter Cronkite's voice talking about the Haynsworth Supreme Court nomination.

"What's the occasion?" Stephen asked.

"I had an epiphany." I smiled.

"Really, what was it?"

"Joan said that the reason I get angry at you when you order from the top of the menu is because I feel I'm not allowed to do that and it's not fair that you do it when I can't," I said.

"Of course!" He laughed.

October 24, 1969

≫≫≪≪

Sitting in the waiting room admiring the white peonies in a tall cut-glass vase, I thought about my father. In the last few years he had thought he was dying a few times and said, "Take care of Mom." I had wanted to yell at him: "All you ever think about is taking care of her. You're my father and you're dying. Why can't you say, 'I love you' or 'Be good to yourself' or 'I'm proud of you.' Why is your last communication to me the same as it has been my whole life? 'You're not on my mind; I'm only interested in your mother.'"

"Hi, Rose," Joan greeted me. Shaken from my trance, I greeted her. "Hello Joan," I half-smiled as I walked into her consulting room. Joan and I had been talking about my father's failing health on and off for a while so she knew it was just a matter of time.

"He died," I whispered through my sobs.

"I'm sorry," she said, leaning forward in her chair.

"It's been so long that he's been getting weaker and weaker. They called me from the rehab hospital and said they sent him to the emergency room," I explained. "By the time I got there he was gone."

"I'm so sorry."

Tears were falling down my face, but I wasn't sorry my father was dead. The last few years had been unbearable for him. He couldn't tie his own shoes or walk and he was incontinent. He was miserable, yet he didn't want to die. But I was glad he finally let go.

185

"It's not sad that he died." I took a tissue from her coffee table and blew my nose. "Going on would have meant more pain and indignity. I'm just sorry he never talked to me about how he felt about me. It was all about my mother until his last breath."

"Yes."

I laid down on the couch and cried so hard I could not catch my breath. I sat up to get another tissue and to calm myself. I imagined Joan leaning forward in her chair as if she were readying herself to administer CPR. After a few minutes I composed myself enough to lie down again and speak. My head throbbed.

"My father never looked at me. He never complimented me on how I dressed or communicated any pleasure at my budding womanliness or my accomplishments. It's funny I just remembered a dream about him. I dreamt that my father had an apartment in my building, but he doesn't live there. It is full of old furniture and it's all dirty and there are rats in there. It's been there for years, untouched. I tell him I will clean it all out for him, but he angrily rejects my offer."

"What did you feel when you woke up?"

"Frustrated, hopeless and angry," I said.

"I think you and your father in the dream are both parts of you."

"What? What do you mean?" I turned my head toward her chair.

"Well you want to clean out the old stuff and he doesn't want to. He wants to hold onto it. I think that's really your conflict. Part of you has moved on—you've got Stephen and your life is changing. But part of you is still holding onto all the old anger and resentment for the things you didn't get from your father."

It was as if I hadn't been wearing my glasses and everything looked blurry and then Joan handed them to me and everything came into focus. My mind turned to thinking about Stephen.

"I want to marry him," I said.

"Really!" she exclaimed.

"I love him. No one has ever loved me and understood me like he does. Even when I have one of my angry episodes, he doesn't run away. He doesn't let me get away with it, but he doesn't run away."

"Well, that's exciting, but our time is up for now."

⇶⇇

When I walked out of her building, I headed for the Plaza Funeral Home to meet Linda and make the arrangements for my father's funeral. My mother was too distraught to make any decisions. Linda was the closest to a sister I had; she knew my parents almost as long as I did. I was relieved that she was going to be with me when I decided on the coffin and all the details of the funeral.

Guilty that I'd gone to my therapy appointment the day after my father died, I consoled myself. Talking to Joan had been a balm and the old resentment toward my father had been drained away—at least temporarily. I didn't get what I wanted from my father, but Joan and I had cleaned the wound and it was no longer festering. It was going to hurt for a while, but eventually it was going to heal. After all, I had Stephen and Joan.

December 11, 1969

Rocking back and forth in Joan's rocker, I was humming, "Sweet Caroline."

I smiled to myself as thought about Stephen. I knew we both wanted to get married. We talked about having children all the time, but neither of us proposed.

"Hi, Rose," Joan greeted me when she opened the sound-proofed doors to her office.

"Hi, Joan," I greeted her, glad that she probably hadn't heard me humming.

I settled in on the couch.

"I know that Stephen and I are going to get married," I said, "but he hasn't proposed."

"How does that make you feel?" she asked.

"Well, it's annoying." I contorted my face.

"Yes?" she prodded.

"He's shy and although he knows I'm crazy about him he's still too afraid of rejection to ask me. It's so silly," I said.

"What's silly?"

"It's silly that he's afraid to ask me and it's silly that I'm waiting for him!"

"Do you have any doubts that he loves you and wants to marry you?"

"No, that's why it's so silly!"

"So are you going to just keep waiting for him to say it and get angrier?"

"No, I guess I'm not. It's awkward though," I said. I was quiet for a few minutes.

"What are you feeling?" Joan asked.

"I was imagining the scene if I had told my father I was getting married before he died."

"And what did you imagine?"

"'That's nice,' he would say." I chuckled.

We were both quiet.

"What are you feeling?" Joan asked.

"Just sad." I wiped my cheeks.

"Can you talk about it?" She prodded gently.

"There were two different sides to my father.... Well, more of course. But I'm thinking of the side of him that was so symbiotic with my mother that there was no space for me, vs the side of him that took me to see the Keffords and loved them."

"Yes, he was a complicated man," Joan said.

"Will you come to the wedding?" I asked. I closed my eyes tightly, waiting for the answer.

"Have you and Stephen decided to get married?" she asked, sounding surprised.

"No, not yet," I said. "But I know we are going to."

"Why don't we talk about it when the two of you make the decision?"

"But I just want to know that you will come," I said.

"I don't know yet. Let's talk about it," she said.

"Look," I said, "other than Stephen, you're the most important person in my life. I wouldn't be marrying him if it weren't for you. I would have driven him away. So how can you not come to my wedding?"

"I understand," she replied. "I would love to go to your wedding. I'm very happy for you and I want to be there. But as you know, it's complicated."

"Sure. After all you don't want to be sitting next to my Aunt Gus or someone."

She laughed.

"I'm sure you wouldn't put me next to Aunt Gus. But I wouldn't really be comfortable going to the reception. How about if I come to the ceremony so I can see your gown and meet Stephen, but then I'll leave?"

"That feels so good to me, you have no idea." I wiped my cheeks.

"I think I do actually, but our time is up."

⟫⟩⟨⟪

I got off the couch and smiled at Joan, who was already grinning. She looked pleased with herself like someone opening the oven and admiring the crust on a blueberry pie.

Then my thoughts went back to my father. My father wouldn't see me in my wedding gown and wouldn't walk me down the aisle. But it was enough that Joan was going to be there. I smiled to myself thinking of the Passover chant *Dayeinu* (It would have been enough.)

When I got home, Stephen was cooking.

"Hi," I greeted him.

He stopped what he was doing and came over to kiss me.

"Do you think we are going to get married?" I asked.

"Of course!" He smiled and feigned surprise.

"Are you going to ask me?"

He laughed. "You know how I am."

"Someone who won't ask?"

191

"I guess. But you know I want to marry you," he said with wide eyes.

"Yes," I said, leaning my head on his chest. "But I want you to say it. I need you to say it."

"Okay," he said. He lifted my head, so I faced him. "I want to marry you," he said. "Do you want to marry me?"

"Yes!"

Mary Elizabeth

Just before Mary Elizabeth's session, I went to my desk to get a pen. The drawer got stuck and in my attempt to close it, I closed it on my hand. I was about to put ice on it when the doorbell rang. I held my hand as I opened the door for her. I explained that I had hurt my hand and went to get ice. I sat in my big Mission chair leaning on the arm of the chair with an ice bag on my hand while she lay on the couch. My chair was pulled up close to the edge of the couch, so I could hear nuances in tone and see tears that I might not notice if I had been sitting further away. The ice numbed the pain so I listened comfortably.

"I'm feeling good about things at work. I'm putting myself out there at the hospital and volunteering to do things."

I waited a minute to see if she would continue.

"Can you tell me what you're feeling?" I asked gently.

The brown suede pillow on the couch was wet with tears.

"I feel you hurt your hand because I feel so good today. When I feel good you are hurt…."

She was weeping.

"Can you explain that to me? What's the connection? How does you feeling good cause me to be hurt?"

"My mother suffered having me and then was drained by me. I remember once she was in the bathroom and she asked for toilet paper and when she opened the door to take it from me I could see she was

193

bleeding. I don't know if she was having her period or one of her miscarriages."

"But how did your happiness hurt her?"

"She never got what she wanted. Everything good that happened to me just made her feel worse about her own life. I remember seeing a movie about a boxer—his hands were lethal weapons. That's how I felt, like some kind of lethal weapon. My mother's rage was so unpredictable. You never knew when it was going to erupt. I felt I caused it somehow, but I never understood how. I inflicted the harm without knowing what I did to cause the outcome."

I wanted to hug her and tell her I knew exactly what she meant. After all, my mother's rage erupted unpredictably as well. But I knew I couldn't do that. I had to help her understand what her feeling was about. How did her experience get distorted into the notion that her happiness was lethal? I thought about Joan and wondered if she had ever wanted to get out of her chair and hug me.

"But you didn't cause your mother's pain. What makes you feel lethal?"

"I *did* hurt my mother. She experienced me as causing her pain. When I was born she was ripped when I came out. She told me that."

"How did you feel when she told you that?" My eyes opened wide.

Wringing her hands, she said, "It made me feel powerful and dangerous."

"I think it's interesting," I said, "that those two feelings go together."

"You mean if I stop feeling dangerous I will have to give up being powerful?"

"Maybe."

She was sighing deeply and crying. She hugged herself.

"Realizing that is a relief," she said. "It makes clear why I feel I can never have children; I would only hurt them."

I worried about that too. I had gone through years of analysis to make sure I would not be like my mother. I would be different. Tears welled up in my eyes, but Mary Elizabeth could not see them from the couch.

"Feeling good had no connection with my hurting my hand," I said. "I hurt my hand because I rushed and was not paying attention."

"What about my mother? I did cause her pain in her life. She felt upset when I was the valedictorian like she had been in high school."

"Your mother was jealous of you," I said, "but she made a decision. She decided to forego college to get married. And she could have gone to college later. You didn't cause her unhappiness. She blamed you for decisions she made."

I remembered the day my mother screamed at me for buying the wrong ketchup when I was nine years old. She left me a note and money to go to the A&P to buy it after I got home from school. I went to the store and knew exactly where the ketchup was located because I often ran errands for her. When I stood in front of the ketchup shelf, there were no 16-ounce bottles of Heinz, which was our usual brand. I had to choose between a 16-ounce Ann Page and a 32-ounce Heinz. Knowing that my mother would yell at me if I made the wrong choice, I stood in the aisle for a long time with temples pulsating. Finally, I went for the size over the brand. When I returned home, my mother was there.

"Did you get it?" she asked before saying hello. She was changing from her work clothes to her *shmata*.

"Well…," I was biting my lip. "They didn't have Heinz in the regular size, only the big one. So, I bought Ann Page in the regular size." I stood slouched, waiting for the explosion.

195

"What!" my mother shouted. "What's wrong with you? You know we only use Heinz."

She picked up the brown bag with the wrong ketchup and threw it at me.

"Return this and get the right ketchup."

I was a child. If you send a child to the supermarket, she may not make the same judgment call an adult would make.

Now I returned my attention to Mary Elizabeth.

"But she was ripped," she said, "when I came out of her womb. I did cause her pain."

I grimaced in pain, feeling a contraction in my Kegel muscle and imagining how it would feel to have a tear between my vagina and my anus. I'd been thinking about having a baby for a while and most of my anxiety about it was focused on the episiotomy.

"Part of choosing to have a child," I said, while rubbing my eyes, "involves choosing to suffer the pain of childbirth. You didn't do anything to cause her pain. She just had a difficult childbirth."

I wondered if you can be ripped even if you have an episiotomy.

"She never chose to have children," she said, covering her face with her hands. She was a religious Catholic so she felt it was a sin to use birth control."

A surge of fury bubbled up in me. All these men in the Catholic Church telling women they have to give birth to babies they don't want. The Pope and all the lackey priests tell women to endure something they know nothing about. I bit my lip.

"I understand," I said. "I think you're right that she felt she had no choice but to have children although she didn't want to. But that doesn't mean *you* caused her unhappiness."

I thought about my mother yelling at me; I could never do anything right. But it wasn't true; I was a child and she was expecting too much of me.

"Oh my God... It wasn't my fault...."

She wept, hugging herself to give comfort where there had been none before.

"It wasn't my fault," she said heaving.

"No, it wasn't."

"Oh my God."

She jumped up from the couch and looked at me in astonishment.

"That feeling that you're going to stick me with something," she said. "I think I know what it is."

I sat up straight in my chair.

"I think my mother used to stick me with pins," she said excitedly as if she had just solved a mystery, "when she changed my diaper."

"What do you mean?"

"I always feel it on my side." She pointed to her hip. "It's where you would put a safety pin in a diaper. She didn't want me. She was angry that she had to deal with me. That feels right. We're going to have to stop aren't we?"

"Yes, how does that feel?"

"Bad. I don't want to have to go. I love you."

"I know it's hard to stop." *God I know!* "But you'll be back tomorrow."

⟫⟫⟪⟪

I wanted to say: "I love you too." I didn't want to stop either. But I knew I couldn't do that. It wasn't just because all my training taught me not to say things like that to patients. Finally, I understood the pur-

197

pose of the rule. It wasn't about being arbitrary and sadistic, the way I had experienced it for so long. Although she consciously wanted me to say it, I didn't know what it would mean to her unconsciously. She might feel I was not like her parents because I didn't want to push her away. But, on the other hand, she might feel as if I was out of control, and be frightened.

Mary Elizabeth felt her mother was out of control with anger and was sadistic when she changed her diapers. I remembered my mother slapping me across the face because I responded to her screaming at me with, "But ..." She was out of control too. Her face was scarlet and the veins on her temples were inflated by the pressure of the blood against the vessels; I thought she would have a stroke. And it would be my fault.

Mary Elizabeth worried that she could be sadistic to a child and she had begged off having any; she was afraid she'd be like her mother. I had the same anxiety; I wondered if I was capable of being out of control and sadistic to my child.

Dave

Dave was referred by the Theodore Reik Consultation Center. It offered low-fee psychoanalysis and psychotherapy in order to supply patients to analysts-in-training like me. Eager for the experience, I agreed to see him for six dollars per session. The intake report said he was a 26-year-old graduate student.

When I opened the door to my waiting room to meet him, I was surprised that despite a mustache and beard he looked like a college student, because he was thin and he was dressed like a motherless boy. He wore a wrinkled long-sleeve cotton shirt and a hooded sweat shirt without a coat despite the nasty March weather.

"Hello, Dave, it's nice to meet you," I said.

"Hello," he said without a smile.

He settled in a chair across from mine.

"I have two degrees from the New School—a masters in the arts and a second one in psychology," he said pulling his wool cap down further on his long unkempt hair.

I nodded.

"Can you tell me a little about your background apart from school?" I asked.

"Well, I grew up in Queens and I'm an only child. I went to Queens College before the New School and now I'm getting my doctorate at the Graduate Center in clinical psychology."

"And what brings you to therapy?" I asked.

"Well, I think I should experience psychotherapy as part of my training," he said.

"Is there any other reason?"

I noticed his hairy leg peeking out of the gap between his shrunken jeans and his socks.

"I have a girlfriend," he said after a long silence. "But I have no interest in having sex with her." He crossed his arms and scanned the books on my shelves.

"Can you tell me more about that?" I asked.

"Well, sometimes," he said with hesitation, "I want to have sex with her, but if she wants to have sex with me then I'm turned off."

"What is it about her being interested in having sex with you that turns you off?" I asked.

"I feel like she just wants to use me to satisfy her own needs," he said nodding.

"Does anything come to mind about someone using you for her own needs?"

He smirked. "Yes, my mother was all about getting me to do things for her own needs instead of mine."

"Can you give me an example?" I asked.

There was a long pause. He changed positions in his chair.

"My mother loved *at* me," he said. "She wanted my love—but not so that I could feel good about her—she wanted it for herself." He rubbed the back of his neck.

"Can you give me an example?"

There was another long pause.

"She always wanted me to eat, but the things in the refrigerator were rotten. She just wanted to get rid of what was in the refrigerator."

My mind turned to my mother and our refrigerator. I remembered the night that Linda slept at our house. She wanted a snack at about 11:30—after my parents were asleep. We went into the kitchen without turning on the light and opened the refrigerator, reminding each other to be quiet. Linda found some salami. She took it out and started to slice it when the light went on and my mother stood at the entrance to the kitchen in her skimpy nightgown with her eyes blinking from the fluorescent light.

"What do you think you're doing?" she hissed with fists clenched.

"Mom, we were just getting a snack," I said with raised brows and eyes opened wide.

Linda stood frozen with a knife in her hand.

"That salami," my mother yelled, "is for tomorrow's lunch." She pointed to the salami as she yelled at Linda with squinted eyes.

"I'm sorry, Mrs. Winer, I'm really sorry," Linda mumbled with tears in her eyes.

Now, I turned my attention back to Dave's mother.

"So your girlfriend is like your mother?" I asked.

"Yes," he agreed, "she wants sex for herself. It's not about me. It's about her pleasure."

"So you feel that if she wants the pleasure of sex she cannot be interested in your pleasure as well?"

"That's right," he said nodding agreement with himself.

"Well, our time is up for now. Would you like to come back?"

"Yes, I want to come twice a week," he said.

"Good, then I will see you again on Tuesday."

※»)»«(«

I sat still in my chair when Dave left the office. He was so distant and without emotion. I had been reading Harry Guntrip's description of the schizoid personality and Dave seemed to fit exactly. He needed to create distance to protect himself from feeling consumed by his girlfriend and I understood this was going to play out with me if he kept coming.

April 15, 1970

Rocking back and forth in the waiting room, I was reading about the Apollo 13 astronauts lost in space. I tried to imagine their terror at the possibility of circling the earth for the rest of their lives. But then my thoughts turned to Dave's first dream: *"I was in a room studying because someone was coming."* Dave said the dream took place in the room he had had as a boy. There was a desk and papers all over it. He was writing a play.

The dream was so short; so stark. I didn't know what to think about it. My dreams were usually much longer and more complicated. Joan and I took them apart piece by piece and I associated to each segment. But this was so simple. He was isolated and there was no action. I thought about how Joan might deal with the dream. What was the feeling in the dream? At first I thought there was none, but then I realized that avoidance is a feeling and that was the essence of the dream. I had grappled with what to say to him.

"Does anything come to mind about trying to avoid someone?" I had finally asked.

"Yes, my girlfriend Erica asked me to help paint a friend's house, but I don't want to do it. I'm going to tell her I have to study." He said that when he was a kid, if someone was coming to visit, he would go to great lengths, offering all kinds of excuses, to avoid any social interaction.

Now, the Lilliputian emerged from Joan's office. She was wearing a red suit with a short jacket that was flattering to her stature and, for the first time since I'd been seeing her, she looked happy. I wondered if she'd found a man—maybe a tall man who liked towering above her and lifted her up to kiss her. Or maybe it was a short guy who finally found a woman shorter than him and fell madly in love with her.

"Hi, Rose," Joan greeted me warmly. She was wearing a lime-green dress that emphasized her dirty blond hair; she looked vibrant.

"Does the Lilliputian have a new boyfriend?" I asked.

Joan grinned. "What?"

"I always thought of that patient as a Lilliputian because she's so short. She looked happy when she came out of your office today so I imagined she has a boyfriend and that's why she's happy."

"You have a wonderful imagination," she said with a chuckle.

"I have this new patient," I said ignoring her observation. "He said his mother fed him when *she* was hungry. One time she told him he should eat the food in the refrigerator. But he says the food was spoiling and she just wanted to get rid of it."

"That's quite a mother," Joan said.

I thought about the roast beef sandwiches on stale rye bread my mother used to put in a crumpled brown paper bag for me to take to school. When I bit into the sandwich these gray, gristly pieces of roast beef fell out onto my lap. Other kids traded sandwiches, but no one ever wanted to trade with me. I was ashamed; everyone could see my mother did not love me.

"My patient told me an incredible story. He said that one of Houdini's stunts was to allow someone to punch him in the stomach as hard as he could. He could prepare himself so that he was able to take the punch. One day a man rang his bell and Houdini opened the door. The

204

man punched him in the stomach as hard as he could and Houdini died—he was caught by surprise."

"Is that true?" she asked.

"No, I checked it out this morning in a biography I found at the NYU library. I'd heard of Houdini, but I didn't know if that was the way he died or if it was the patient's revision. It turns out that Houdini actually died of peritonitis as a result of a ruptured appendix. He reconstructed Houdini's death so that it represented his own vision of his life."

"Isn't the unconscious amazing?"

"Yes, he doesn't want to be caught by surprise and I think having feelings about me feels like he's opening himself up to be killed. He has to remain prepared to resist. But I want to have an impact on him. I want to help him transform his life in the way you've helped me. And increasingly I realize that he's reigniting my anger toward my father. My father was so focused on pleasing my mother that I feel I could never have an impact on him."

"So you're worried about getting angry at this patient?"

"Exactly." I nodded. "He also pays late and that infuriates me because he's only paying me six dollars a session!"

"Yes, low-fee patients can bring up a lot of feelings when they act out," she said.

My chest tightened. "I'm a low-fee patient," I said. "After all, I started at the clinic."

"Yes, but you got a job to pay for your sessions and you always pay on time," she said.

"But I don't pay your full fee," I said.

"Yes, but I think you're confusing two very different dynamics. Your patient's whole character structure is based on withholding and not wanting to give any satisfaction. You are the opposite, you want to give me as much as you possibly can.... As much as I will allow you to. That's completely different."

"I'm glad you know that."

"I assume you've been talking to Anne about him." Joan said.

"Yes. Sure."

"Look, patients bring up feelings for us. There's no way around that. It's just part of the work. As long as you know what he's tapping into, you'll be fine."

"I'm worried. I have such a short fuse," I said.

"You're not your mother; you're not anything like her. Between talking to Anne and seeing me, you will be fine."

"How do you know?" I asked.

"You aren't alone in this. Anne and I will help you."

I sighed.

"Joan, I love you. What would I do without you?"

"We're going to have to stop for now."

Supervision, Continued

Excited to tell Anne about my sessions with Dave, I walked fast from the subway to Anne's office. It was a warm spring day and I savored the warmth of the sun on my bare arms.

"Dave told me a dream!" I said with a grin as soon as I sat down across from Anne.

"'I was in a room studying because someone was coming.' He said it was the room he had as a boy. There was a desk and papers all over it. He was writing a play."

"He's frightened," she said, "of being intruded upon and taken over by his girlfriend. He can't let anyone in or they will take him over. He must have had a very intrusive mother."

"Well," I said, "that means he's not going to take me in either, right?"

"Yes, he's going to be tough. Interpretations will feel like attacks to him."

"He told me he didn't want to satisfy his girlfriend sexually because he's afraid the experience of orgasm would make her insatiable. He's afraid of being devoured by her voracious appetite."

"Poor guy," she said. "What has he told you about his mother?"

"He said she filled the refrigerator with rotten food and tried to get him to eat it. She told him it was good for him."

"Oy!" she exclaimed. Her tone was so empathic. No matter what Dave felt, it seemed, Anne could always put his feelings in the context of what he experienced as a child. I wanted to understand what made her able to feel more empathy for him than I could.

"You know I was thinking about why I don't feel more identified with him. Why don't I feel the desire to hug him or say something consoling?" I asked.

Anne took off her glasses and smiled at me.

"This guy is cold and off-putting," she said. "He doesn't want you to get near him; he's too afraid. So it's not surprising that he doesn't engender warm and fuzzy feelings in you. Remember I'm not in the room with him so I can see what's going on underneath without feeling the impact of his lack of affect. That's how he protects himself. He doesn't want to be affected by you."

"I feel so distant when I'm with him. It's the polar opposite of what I feel with Mary Elizabeth," I said.

"Yes, of course. The hard thing working with someone like him is to try to stay attached despite all of their distance and denial of connection."

"I just realized it's a transference dream!" I said. "He's going to act like I'm not there just like he makes believe he's studying in the dream. Ugh."

She leaned forward in her chair and smiled. "Yes, that's right."

"There's another problem," I said. "I'm using him for my own purposes as well—to get clinical experience. I am not giving him a low fee just because I want to help him. I'm accepting the low fee because I need the experience."

"Look, there's nothing wrong with getting something from someone else," Anne said. "You are also giving him a lot. The problem is that he had a mother who didn't see him as separate. She used him as if he were just a function—a way of cleaning her refrigerator. You are not doing that."

Sally

Since our income had been growing, Stephen encouraged me to find an office outside of our apartment, so when a studio apartment became available at an affordable rent in our building in June 1970, I rented it.

Sally was the first patient I saw in my new office. My colleague Jessica had referred her to me. She said, "She's really smart and a great person. You're going to love her." When I opened the door to the waiting room to invite her in, I saw a tall, thin woman with stylishly cut gray hair. She was dressed simply in black slacks and a sleeveless turtleneck. There was something elegant, almost aristocratic in the way she carried herself when she got up from glancing at a magazine and entered my office.

"Hello, Sally, please come in." I invited her to sit wherever she was comfortable. There was an analytic couch that I had found at a Mennonite furniture store in Pennsylvania, a rocker close to my chair, and a Mission chair across from mine. She chose the Mission chair and put her bag on the coffee table that separated us. I sat in my oak chair, smiled at her, but remained silent. If she had never been in treatment before, I might have waited a minute and then asked, "So tell me what brought you to see me." But since Jessica, the colleague who referred her, told me she was a psychoanalyst, I waited for her to tell me why she came.

"You're pretty cold, aren't you—silent and cold. But maybe that's not bad. Maybe that will be more analytic and help the transference come out faster than if you were warm and fuzzy."

I didn't imagine myself as "silent and cold." That was the last thing I wanted to be. I thought I was warm and giving her the space to present herself. But before I could respond to her, she continued talking.

"Let me give you my history."

Her face was expressionless as she pulled up her right pants leg to show me an atrophied calf with a large grayish scar that extended from her ankle to her knee.

"When I was five, I was playing in front of my house. I ran into the street after a ball and a car hit me. I almost lost my right leg; it was crushed. I was in the hospital for months. They saved the leg, but I have this scar and a limp." She smiled curtly.

I hadn't noticed the limp when she came the short distance from the waiting room into my office. I made an inaudible noise and knitted my brows.

"Then when I was fifteen, my father was in a car accident and he died," she said in a matter-of-fact tone.

I gasped in disbelief that so much tragedy had befallen her at such a young age. But she continued telling the story without affect, as if she were giving me a chronology of what she did over the weekend. I wanted to say something empathic to her, but I would have had to interrupt her to do it. So I decided to listen silently until she gave me an opportunity to speak.

When she finished telling me the history she thought was relevant for me to know, she turned to telling me about her present life.

"I'm a psychoanalyst and I have a husband, a 25-year-old son and a 21-year-old daughter."

"What are their names?" I asked.

"My husband's name is Jonathan, he's Jewish; my son is Robert and my daughter is Carol."

I smiled and nodded.

"I've come because I'm depressed. I was terribly depressed a few years ago and went into therapy. It helped, but I'm depressed again and I'm also worried about my son. He doesn't have a job and I'm afraid he's not doing the right things to get one. Also, I'm going to be sixty and I feel terrible about it...."

I was about to ask her what was so terrible about being sixty. But before I framed the question, she spoke.

"The thing is that I think there's something wrong with my brain." For the first time, she got teary. "I used to remember everything. But now I take notes on everything because I'm afraid to forget; I walk into a room and forget why I came. I go to get the car and realize I forgot the keys. I know something is wrong with me."

My impulse was to reassure her. I wanted to blurt out: "Oh, that's nothing. I do that all the time."

Sally continued in a voice that sounded frightened. "I think I may be getting dementia. I always remembered *everything* and now I have to make lists to remember things."

I cannot remember the names of things either. It is a running joke with Stephen, whose sarcasm sometimes verges on sadism. We had an episode just before Sally's session.

"'Dancing in the Dark...'" Who sang that? I can't remember his name. It's Fred something," I said.

"What's his sister's name?" Stephen responded

"I can't remember his name, how the hell can I remember his sister's name?"

"It's something you climb," he prompted.

"Fred Steps."

"No." He laughed.

"Fred Astaire!"

Now, I resisted the impulse to reassure Sally because it might have made her feel that I was not really hearing her. I did not want to trivialize her anxiety. There *could* be something wrong with Sally's brain.

"I went to a neurologist," she said, "and he said there was nothing wrong. But I heard about this cognitive test regimen you can take and I'm going to do it."

I wanted to say: "That sounds like a good idea." But she didn't want to be interrupted—she didn't even take a breath.

"I don't want anyone who knows me to know about this. I came to you because you're not involved in my circle. I won't tell any of my friends except Jessica and I'm terrified of them finding out."

I wanted to reassure her about the rule of confidentiality, but I was stung by her pointing out that I wasn't "in her circle." I wondered what that was about. Was she putting me down or was I feeling paranoid for some reason? And she's a therapist; she knows all about confidentiality. I knew that what I should say was: "What's the terror about?" But she had continued talking so fast that I would have had to cut in to ask her. I looked at the clock and the session was over.

"You haven't said anything all session," she said. "You just sat there—a silent analyst. I guess you're quite orthodox or maybe you're just inexperienced."

Feeling a simultaneous eruption of self-doubt and outrage, I wanted to say *something*, but the session was over. I was afraid I would blurt out something angry and defensive: "You haven't stopped for a breath. I couldn't say anything without interrupting you." I dug my nails into the palms of my hands. I knew I had to get over feeling insulted and say something supportive to her.

"Well, we're going to have to stop in a minute. But I think it's a good thing that you've come because it sounds as if you've experienced a great deal of trauma and loss. Turning sixty seems to be a catalyst for re-experiencing those feelings again."

"I can only come once a week. It takes me almost an hour to get here.

"That's fine," I said taking deep breath. "I'll see you next week."

>>><<<

When Sally got up to leave the office I noticed the limp. I sat immobilized for a few minutes after she left and thought about what I was feeling and what Jessica had said about her.

I didn't love her. She was controlling and critical during the session. I wondered about the disparity in our perceptions of Sally. What will Sally tell Jessica about me? I imagined Sally calling her and telling her I was an amateur.

Sally made me feel I was all dressed up with my slip showing. But by the time I got to my apartment and kissed Stephen hello, my feelings of inadequacy had washed away like pebbles in a stream.

Mary Elizabeth

When I opened the door of my office Mary Elizabeth was standing in the waiting room looking out the window. I greeted her and she turned around quickly and had a big smile. She followed me into my office and closed the door.

"I'm so happy to see you," she said. "It's such a beautiful summer day outside."

She handed me a carefully wrapped package with a bow on it.

Orthodox Freudians didn't accept gifts. But Joan did. She accepted them graciously and then analyzed what the gifts meant. So I smiled and did the same thing.

"Would you like me to open it now?" I asked.

"Yes, yes, please open it now." She was smiling excitedly, leaning forward as she sat up on the couch.

I opened the package. It contained three illustrated children's books.

"Thank you. Are they for me?" I asked, raising an eyebrow.

"Yes, they're for you."

Why was she bringing me children's books? I wanted to create the space for this to play out rather than immediately focus on what it meant.

"I want you to read it to me," she said with a big smile.

Joan always asked me to read things when I brought in things for her to read, so I did the same thing.

"Why don't you read to me?" I offered the books.

"Oh, okay." She pouted.

She picked up the first one: *My Love for You*. Sitting on the couch with a forced smile, she started to read aloud. "My love for you..." Her smile turned to tears as soon as she turned the page: "...is bigger than one bear, taller than two giraffes, larger than three blue whales..."

She was crying hard and it was difficult for her to continue. "...wider than four elephants, longer than five pythons." She stopped for a moment trying to catch her breath, and then continued: "My love for you...is deeper than six deep-sea fish, stronger than seven gorillas, mightier than eight lions, heftier than nine hippos. My love for you... is loftier than ten lovebirds soaring high above the clouds, and greater than all of these together... forever." She was sobbing and her nose was running. She reached over to grab a tissue from the dispenser on the round wooden table. She was trying to talk through the sobs.

"Do you understand?"

"Yes."

I wondered if this was the beginning of an erotic transference or whether she had regressed to feeling like a little girl and wanted to have a mother who was comfortable with her love. To my own surprise, I *was* comfortable with her love—whatever it was.

"I love you so much."

I loved her too. But I wanted to let her go on, so I was quiet.

"Let me read you the other one. It's called, *Are You My Mother?*"

It was about a baby bird looking for her mother and mistaking all kinds of animals and things for her mother.

In a child's voice she said, "I want you to lie next to me while I read you the story. I want you to hold me close."

I thought she understood that I was not going to lie down with her or hold her. She was just telling me what she wanted; I was comfortable with that. Mary Elizabeth felt she wasn't allowed to express her love to her mother—her mother kept her oar out. But we had created a space in which she felt safe enough to tell me how much she loved me and what she wanted from me.

Mary Elizabeth was quiet. Maybe she was waiting for my reply. I was calm; I was giving her space.

"Can you tell me what you're feeling?"

She was sobbing again.

"I love you and I want you to lie next to me."

Uh oh, I was surprised; she really wanted me to lie next to her. Part of me wanted to lie next to her, but I thought if I did, I couldn't predict how she would experience it. But if I didn't, she might feel I didn't want her to have a body and I was repulsed by her and wanted her to keep her distance. I decided to share my quandary with her.

"As long as we talk about it, we can figure out what it would mean to you if I lie next to you or don't. If I simply do it, we won't understand it until the potential damage is done."

"I don't want to talk about it. I just want you to lie next to me."

"I know, but we need to talk more about it and unfortunately our time is up for now." I took a deep breath.

⟫⟫⟫⟪⟪⟪

Mary Elizabeth got up from the couch and put the books on my book shelf. She wasn't angry as I might have been years ago with Joan. She turned to me with a smile, tears in her eyes, and walked to the door.

I heard the phone ringing as I walked into our apartment. Stephen picked it up. He said, "Hello." He listened for a minute and then turned and gave the phone to me.

"It's about your mother," he said. "It's not good." His face was ashen.

"Hello," I said, taking the phone from him.

"I'm calling from the emergency room of Maimonides Hospital," a woman's voice said.

"Oh, no!"

"Your mother, Molly Winer is here in the ER. She's had a stroke," she said.

"Shit! Is it bad?" I looked at Stephen pleadingly as if he would be able to keep her alive.

"I can't give you any information about her condition," she said matter-of-factly, "but I suggest that you get here as soon as you possibly can."

"You mean she's dying?"

"I can't give you any information, sorry," she said.

"Okay, thank you."

I turned to Stephen. "She's had a stroke," I said, sobbing. "She could be dying, I have to go to the ER at Maimonides right away." He nodded. I guessed she told him that before he handed over the phone.

"First my father and now her," I wailed. He put his arms around me.

"Yes," he whispered.

"I know you can't stand her..."

"But I don't want her to die," he insisted.

"I know, sorry." I moved from his embrace and got my purse.

"I'll go with you," he said, and put out his hand.

An hour later we found my mother in the emergency room at Maimonides Hospital in Brooklyn. It was familiar to me because I had visited my father here so many times before he died. The room was full of Hasidic Jews and Hispanics with nurses and aides milling around. I looked through all the curtains set up around the nurses' station until I found her.

"Hi, Mom," I greeted her and she smiled at me.

Uncle Morris was standing next to my mother's bed in the cubicle. He lived in my mother's apartment building and called 911; he came with her in the ambulance.

"Hi, Uncle Morris, thanks for bringing Mom here," I said, kissing him on his unshaved cheek.

"It was just lucky," he said in his thick Hungarian accent. "I rang her bell, and she didn't answer." He rubbed the back of his neck. "I knew she was home, so I waited a few minutes and then I heard her voice crying, 'Help.'"

"Thank you!" I wiped my eyes with a tissue.

"She had a stroke," he said.

Getting Married

I had an image of what my wedding would be, but it had given way because of my mother's stroke. I wanted to make sure that we got married before she died. But Stephen and I still had some tense conversations about what kind of wedding we were going to have.

First, there was the discussion about the ring.

"No, I won't wear a ring," he said shaking his head.

"But why? If I wear a ring and you don't, then I belong to you and you don't belong to me," I said sobbing.

"That's ridiculous, we are getting married and we both belong to each other. I don't have to wear a ring to belong to you," he scoffed.

"I just don't get it, why do you refuse to wear a ring? Just explain it to me and I won't feel so bad about it," I said.

"I can't explain it to you. I don't know why," he said with misty eyes.

"You have your father's ring, why don't you want to wear it?" I asked.

"I just told you, I don't know why. I just know I won't wear a ring," he said. "Do you think I will cheat on you if I don't wear a ring?"

"No... I don't think you will cheat on me," I said. "But it goes against everything that we both believe in for me to wear a ring and you not to."

"Wearing a ring has nothing to do with what we believe in," he insisted. "I just hate wearing any jewelry and don't want to wear a ring."

"But why, just explain it to me."

"I don't know, maybe it has to do with my father. He wore a ring," Stephen said.

"So, you just want to be defiant!?" My eyes bulged.

"I just don't want to, that's all," he said.

"Do you want me to wear a veil too?" I thought of Rebecca veiling her face when she was first brought to Isaac to be his wife. It was one of the few Bible stories I knew besides Job!

Stephen snickered. "Come on, this isn't about sexism. It isn't about putting you down. I just don't want to wear a ring on my finger."

I heard Joan's voice in my head: "Do you REALLY want to have a big fight about this?"

"Okay," I said, sniffling. "I'm not happy about it, but I don't want this to ruin everything."

"Also, I don't want a big kosher wedding with all your mother's friends," he said.

"No, I don't think we have to worry about that anymore," I said.

"Why is that?"

"She's lost all that energy since her stroke. She doesn't care about what her friends think."

"What about Gus?" Stephen asked.

"No, since the stroke she doesn't even seem to worry about what Gus thinks. Anyway, she's going to need whatever money she has for a private nursing facility so she can't give us money for the wedding, even if she wanted to."

"I'd be perfectly happy with a very small group and lunch afterwards," he said.

"Okay, I don't care about a big wedding, I just want to marry you."

Stephen put his arms around me and held me tight. "Me too."

Once we decided it was going to be a small one-ring ceremony, we made an appointment with Rabbi Dennis Rothstein of the Village Temple for a pre-marriage consultation. Rabbi Rothstein was not much older than we were and wore a wedding ring. The Village Temple was a Reform synagogue, but Rabbi Rothstein wore a *yamulke* at all times. Ours was going to be his first wedding and he was eager to explain everything to us.

He greeted us and asked us to sit down in the chairs facing his desk.

"Well, it's very nice to meet you both," he said with his hands folded in front of him on the desk.

"It's nice to meet you too," we both said, not exactly in unison.

I thought about Jake. Dennis Rothstein did not strike me as someone who studied Aramaic.

"Are you both Jewish?" he asked.

"Yes, we are," I answered. "But neither of us is particularly religious."

He smiled. "How long have you been together?" he asked.

"Over a year," Stephen said.

"Okay, then let me explain the process of a Jewish marriage," he said.

"On the Shabbat of the week of your marriage, it's customary for the groom to have an *aliyah*. Do you know what that is?" he asked.

"Yes, I know what that is," Stephen said stiffly. "My parents were the founders of a synagogue in Queens."

"That's nice." The rabbi smiled and tilted his head as if he was reconsidering who Stephen was. He leaned forward on his desk.

"But I don't, so why don't you explain it," I said.

"An *aliyah* is an honor given to the groom at the Shabbat service," the Rabbi explained. "He recites a blessing over the Torah reading."

"So it's only for the groom?" I asked, straightening up in my chair.

"Well," he said, raising his eyebrows, "that's the tradition."

"What about the bride being veiled?" I asked. "Do you enforce that tradition as well?"

"We don't *enforce* tradition," Rabbi Rothstein said, leaning back, "it's up to you if you'd like a veil."

I nodded and bit my lip.

"The ceremony itself lasts 20 to 30 minutes, and consists of the *kiddushin* and the *nisuin*," the rabbi said. "For the *kiddushin*, the bride approaches and circles the groom. Two blessings are recited over wine: one the standard blessing over wine and the other regarding the commandments related to marriage. The man then places the ring on the woman's finger and says, "Be sanctified to me with this ring in accordance with the law of Moses and Israel."

I swallowed hard. Stephen turned to look at me, but then decided to continue looking at the rabbi.

"After the *kiddushin* is complete, the *ketubah* is read aloud," he said.

"What's the *ketuba*?" I asked.

"It's the marriage contract. It provides for a money settlement payable to the wife in the event of divorce or at the husband's death—things like that. It's all about protecting the wife."

"What about protecting the husband?" I asked.

"Well … ," he said. The rabbi smiled and pushed his chair back from the desk. It's an ancient document. So it assumes women have no source of income and limited possibilities for remarriage."

I turned to Stephen. "We don't want that, do we?"

"No," he said. "We don't want a *ketuba*."

"You can revise it if you want. Reform Jews are not as insistent on the *ketuba* as Conservative or Orthodox," he said. "Are you going to have a two-ring ceremony?"

"No," Stephen said looking at the floor, "we're having one ring for the bride."

"Okay," the rabbi said. He looked at me to see if I was having a reaction. "After the ring is given, the *nisuin* proceeds. I will recite the *sheva brakhos*, the seven blessings."

"What about the one thanking God for creating man in his own image?" I asked.

"What do you mean?" the rabbi asked.

"I don't want that in my wedding. Please change it to 'man and woman'."

"Okay…" he said, biting his cheek and taking a note. "The couple then drinks the wine. Okay?"

"Yes," Stephen said patting my hand, "that's fine."

"Then the groom smashes a glass with his right foot, to symbolize the destruction of the Temple. Okay?"

"Yes, that's fine," I said. I turned and smiled at Stephen who smiled back.

When we left the rabbi's office, we walked toward our apartment.

"I want to explain something to you," Stephen said.

"About what?"

"About my feelings about Judaism."

"Yes?"

"I mentioned to you that my parents founded a synagogue, but it wasn't about religion. It was about socializing with their friends," he said. "They were gone two nights a week and most of Saturday and left me with my grandmother." He stopped walking and turned to face me, weeping. "My *bar mitzvah* was the worst day of my life."

I took his hand and kissed him on the cheek.

"They invited all their friends and the whole thing was their production. It had nothing to do with me. I ended up in the basement taking checks out of envelopes."

I squeezed his hand.

"I don't want to wear my father's ring, I don't want to have a big wedding with your mother's friends, I don't want to wear a *yarmulke* and I don't want a *ketuba!*" Drops rolled down his cheeks.

"Okay," I said, kissing his tears. "You don't have to wear a ring; we are having a small wedding; and we aren't having a *ketuba*."

"Good!"

"But what's the problem with wearing a *yarmulke*?" I asked.

"In my parents' synagogue they never wore *yarmulkes*. Reform Jews don't wear them."

"Well, obviously," I insisted, "they do—because the Rabbi wears one. And that's one thing I can't compromise on. You have to wear a *yarmulke!*"

He was silent for a moment. "Okay, okay. I'll wear a *yarmulke*."

⤜⟫⟪⤛

On August 1, 1970, we stood under the *chuppah* that looked like a large *talit* stretched over four poles. Stephen's friend Tod was the best man and Linda was the maid of honor. My mother stood next to me smiling, but she did not say anything. I was not sure what she was understanding. Stephen's mother, Adele, stood next to him. It was a small chapel with red upholstered seats and a Torah ark cabinet made of birch and poplar wood with mahogany stain. In front of the cabinet was the *bimah*, also made of birch and poplar. Rabbi Rothstein recited each of the seven blessings:

"*Barukh atah Hashem, Eloheynu, melekh ha-olam*, Blessed art thou LORD, our God, King of the Universe who has created everything for his glory.

Barukh atah Hashem, Eloheynu, melekh ha-olam, Blessed art thou LORD, our God, King of the Universe who fashioned the Man and Woman in His image..."

Stephen and I were facing Rabbi Rothstein so I could not see Joan in the back of the chapel, but I had caught a glance of her when I walked down the aisle to the front. I knew she was there.

September 9, 1970

Walking from the subway to Joan's office, I was humming a new Neil Diamond song, "Cracklin' Rosie."

When I opened the door to the waiting room, the dog was barking and I wondered if something had scared or surprised him. I could hear Joan's daughter trying to calm him.

Joan emerged from her office, but she had not been seeing a patient. She looked pale. I had not seen her since the wedding. I knew she had come back from vacation the previous week, so I expected her to have a tan. I squinched my mouth in a twinge of concern, but I knew if I asked her how she was feeling she would tell me she was fine.

"I was visiting my mother. She can't even play bingo. She doesn't know where to put the chip when they call out the number."

"That must be painful to watch." She squinted.

"I know that's painful to some people. But ironically I feel this is the first time she's ever appreciated what I do for her. Her mood is good. She's smiley and nice even though she doesn't understand what's happening. When I take her for a walk she holds onto me and when I buy her a chocolate ice cream pop she's genuinely grateful. So oddly enough I don't find it painful so see her decline. It makes me feel more loving toward her. I want to make sure she's comfortable and not in any pain."

"Strange how dementia can change some people's personality for the better—at least for a while," she said.

"She tells me she's happy to see me and thanks me for coming. She never did that when she was lucid. But I just remembered a dream. I was in the living room with my college roommates and I get hysterical and I pee in my pants. But I'm not upset. Carole says, 'You're all wet.' But I'm still not upset. I say, '"It's no big deal."'"

"What was the feeling when you woke up?"

"Calm. It's strange." I raised one eyebrow.

"What comes to mind about someone telling you you're all wet?" she asked.

"That's funny." I chuckled. "I hadn't thought of it that way. It's as if she's telling me I don't know what I'm talking about, but I'm not upset at her telling me that."

"You were telling me about your mother and how you feel about her not being able to play bingo and not knowing who you are."

"Yes, in the dream Carole is being critical of me and I'm not upset about it." Suddenly I remembered that I used to pee in my pants at night.

"When I was a kid I used to dream I was sitting on the toilet and I'd pee and then I was so afraid of my mother that I would get up in the middle of the night and change the sheets and hide the wet ones until morning and sneak them out of the house and take them to the laundromat."

"Now it's your mother who's peeing in her pants—literally or figuratively."

"Yes. And I'm not upset about it...." I smiled.

We both were silent for a few moments.

"Stephen was disappointed we couldn't go on a honeymoon," I said.

"What about you?" Joan asked.

"I wanted to have a honeymoon in France, but I couldn't leave my mother alone when she was in such a bad way."

"Maybe not, but that doesn't preclude having feelings about it. Does it?" she asked with a smile in her voice.

"No.... I wanted to go. But, I would have felt guilty the whole time.... It wouldn't have been fun." I crossed my arms.

"But it's disappointing, isn't it?" she asked softly.

"Yes," I said as a tear dripped down my cheek.

"We're going to have to stop."

>>><<<

When I walked out of Joan's building it was raining, and I didn't have an umbrella. But I didn't want to wait for it to stop so I ran to the subway in the rain because I was eager to get home and see Stephen.

Mary Elizabeth

As I walked down the hall to my office, I was humming the new Carpenters song, "We've Only Just Begun."

But once I settled into my chair, my thoughts turned to Mary Elizabeth. She had a strong startled response when I opened the door or moved my chair, and intense feeling states that seemed to come from nowhere. She jumped off the couch and felt she had to vomit; she read a book and started to sob uncontrollably; she looked at a picture in my office and felt terror. She described her daily life as "walking on quicksand"—she never knew when she would take a step and be overwhelmed with a sinking feeling. The outline of abuse was there, but Mary Elizabeth couldn't remember any trauma.

The doorbell rang and I rang her in and then got up to greet her. It was a windy November day outside and she had a scarf wrapped around her face. As soon as she lay down, she told me she had had a dream:

> I was in a building that looked like it was on a college campus—the athletic center with a swimming pool or a factory with a vat of water. I was walking around the edge of the water. I was at the head of the line and I said come around here and look at the pool. You can see the water is much deeper. I wanted to dive down to the

deeper part. We dove in. You couldn't tell how deep it was and we went down and then came up. The people fluctuated between being children and adults. When we were children, a younger child was pulling on my top and wanted to tell me that she had been raped. It wasn't horrible, it was matter of fact. It wasn't remarkable. I was surprised she told me. It didn't deter any of us from what we were doing. It was just passed over."

She said she had a sense of doing something forbidden and dangerous, but felt good and enjoyed it.

"How did you feel when you woke up?" I asked.

"I felt 'Oh my God.' I felt badly that I hadn't paid more attention to the child who was raped."

"Who do you think is the child who was raped?" *Oh shit, this is it!* I leaned forward in my chair.

"I don't know if it's me … I feel repulsive. My parents kept their distance from me because they felt repelled by me.… I feel so cold."

She pulled her coat up around her.

"I want to hug you," she whispered. "I know I'm supposed to talk about it and not *do* it."

Mary Elizabeth experienced the golden rule of not touching as confirmation that she was repulsive. I couldn't tolerate her feeling that. I couldn't just let her feel it. I wanted to take the feeling away.

"I don't think you are repulsive," I blurted out. "If you want to hug me, it's fine."

I had violated a cardinal rule of psychoanalysis, but I rationalized it by telling myself there were conditions under which the rule had to be violated. I told myself the most important thing was that Mary Elizabeth not experience me as she experienced her mother, but I should have realized from the dream that the issue was with her father.

She sat bolt upright, her legs carefully parallel and held her winter coat tightly closed as if the buttons would not give her enough protection.

Mary Elizabeth said, "I feel very angry at you, but I don't understand why. I want to hold you, but I want to stab you." She started to cry.

Shocked, I flinched as if I had touched a live wire.

"I just remembered a dream," she said. "There was this motorcycle. This guy used my money to buy it and his fingerprints were on it ... I had the proof; I had the fingerprints."

"What about the fingerprints?" I asked.

"It was the proof of what was done to me."

"What comes to mind about the motorcycle?" I thought to myself: *You should have asked, "What was done to you." You're moving away.*

"I think it's my body."

"I wonder what made you remember the dream just now." *I'm moving away again. Shit.*

"I don't know."

"Maybe it was my saying you could hug me," I said.

"It makes sense, but I don't feel it. Oh, I just remembered I brought something to show you."

She got up and fumbled with her purse and handed me a picture of her and her father when she left for the Peace Corps. Then she lay on the couch and covered herself with her long black coat. She snuggled a bit to get comfortable and carefully laid the coat over her legs so that only her toes peeked through the bottom.

"You and your father look like a couple." He was young looking, thin and smiling with his arm around her.

"When I was about five or six my mother was in the hospital giving birth and I went to the zoo with my father. I was so happy to be there with him. I felt if my mother wasn't around, he and I would be so happy."

Listening to Mary Elizabeth made me remember going to the Keffords with my father, not just because Tom Kefford discussed current events with me and Mary served cookies, but because it was a special time with my father. I was sharing something with him that excluded my mother.

I was so distracted by thinking about the Keffords that I was jolted when Mary Elizabeth started to speak again. I had moved away from the material again. I was afraid to know what she was about to tell me.

"I think I experienced your saying I could hug you as if you wanted to touch me sexually. I feel furious." She was embracing herself on the couch.

The pressure in my temples intensified as if my head was in a vise. I knew theoretically that a woman could transfer her feelings about her father on to me, but it still stunned me. She was experiencing me as if I were her father.

She said she just remembered another dream.

I was in a building that was an institution—a school or a university. I got off the elevator and ran into this little old lady. There was something wrong, I didn't know what—if she'd fallen or what. She was in terrible pain. I picked her up like a child and took her to a bedroom and laid her on a bed. I couldn't comfort her. If I touched her it hurt her. Then there was a room where dance was taught. There were very large windows and light was coming in. The room was almost empty like someone was moving in. I was posing in front of mirrors. My breasts were covered, but down to my groin was this sexy see through thing. I started posing and looking at myself and feeling sexy. Then I saw a man in the hall, it was Dustin Hoffman. I was afraid he would see me half naked and I crouched down and was still. I wanted to cover myself. I put on these trash bags to cover me. Then a little girl climbed in the window and she saw me, but acted like she didn't. She went to the door and went with the man. Then I was teaching in grammar school with children seven, eight, and nine years old. I was angry; I wasn't ready; I was caught. I took it out on the kids, I yelled at them, lashing out at them.

"What comes to mind about being in an institution?" I was relieved that we were talking about the dream and not about my fuck-up.

"It's where everybody is crazy. It was such a little house and how could it be that so much craziness was going on?"

"You mean the institution in the dream is your parents' house?"

"Yes, there were all these crazy things going on in that house."

"Does anything come to mind about a house that was almost empty as if someone was moving in?"

"I want to yell at you, 'Shut up, don't bring that up.'"

"What about the outfit you were wearing in the dream?" I asked.

"I was dressed like a streetwalker or something. I was secretly looking at myself."

"A streetwalker has sex with men for money."

She corrected me. "A streetwalker *wants* to give it to men. When I'm crouched naked in the dream and hiding, I'm not just afraid of being naked, I'm afraid of being caught thinking about sex and my body."

"What comes to mind about thinking about sex and your body?" I asked.

"When I was in elementary school," she said, "the nuns gave us these little pamphlets called 'Lives of the Saints.' Each woman was a saint because she died rather than having sex."

Sitting in my chair behind the couch, I smiled, remembering the girls from St. Rose of Lima walking home from school carrying their "Lives of the Saints" pamphlets. I never understood what was in those pamphlets.

"Can you give me an example?" I asked.

"Sure. How about Saint Agatha? She was handed over to a brothel after she refused to renounce Christianity, and when she refused to accept customers, they tortured her, stretched out on a rack. They crushed her breasts and then cut them off with pincers. Then they rolled her on hot coals and she thanked God when she died."

"What? These stories are meant for children?"

"Yes, they want the girls to know dying is preferable to having sex." She said it casually as if it was obvious.

"So what about *wanting* to have sex?"

"I feel I must have touched my father's penis. Remember you asked me a few weeks ago if I ever saw his penis and I said no, but that's probably not true. I think I must have touched his penis and I can't deal with it because I *wanted* to do it."

"So you think Dustin Hoffman in the dream is your father."

"Yes." She said it as if she were confessing.

"And who do you think the little old lady is. Everything you did hurt her?"

"Funny, I guess that's my mother." She paused. "She was in such pain. I think it's about her being pregnant."

"And what about the little girl who climbed in the window and saw you but acted as if she didn't," I asked.

"It sounds like it's another part of me. Part of me acts like I don't see the other part. Parts of myself are blocked off from other parts."

"Yes," I nodded in agreement. "So she went to the door and went with the man?"

"Yes," she said thoughtfully, "maybe that's the part I can't remember."

"Unfortunately we are going to have to stop."

⫸⫷

Deluged by all the material, I wondered if Mary Elizabeth's guilt was because she *was* molested and it was pleasurable as well as a betrayal. A wave of empathy washed over me. What a terrible bind for a little girl—a flood of excitement dripping with treachery.

Then my thoughts turned to the Catholic Church. I thought being Jewish was complicated, but at least it didn't have any of the blood and gore that seemed to be tied up with female sexuality in Catholicism.

Thoughts of Catholicism inevitably led back to Eleanor. There had been times that I was afraid Mary Elizabeth might kill herself. But now I knew that would never happen. We had gone into rooms in which neither of us had ever been and experienced the love and hate, excitement and guilt.

By the time the bell rang to announce my next patient, I was ready to move on.

Sally

Sally was wearing a black wool suit with a short strand of pearls and reading *Jude the Obscure*, which had been on the shelf in my waiting room.

"Hello Sally," I greeted her.

She carefully returned the book to where it belonged in the bookcase and followed me into my office. I walked over to my chair and, as always, Sally sat in the chair furthest from mine.

"No therapist has a chair higher than her patient. It's such a basic thing."

My mother had slapped me across the face; I could feel the sting in my cheeks. I wondered if my cheeks were red and if she could tell. It had never dawned on me to consider the height of my chair in comparison to the other chairs in the office. But then I remembered the chair I had sat in when I was a patient at Washington Square—the way I'd sank into it and felt humiliated by it. I remembered how angry it had made me toward Joan and that drained my defensiveness away.

"What does it mean if my seat is higher than the others in the room?"

"You must be insecure and need to be higher than your patient. I have never been in a therapist's office with seats of different heights."

What a bitch! I was furious, but then I started second guessing myself. My confidence was shaken. I wanted to talk to Joan about it. Did

I unconsciously try to demean my patients by making my seat higher? Was I making them feel what I had experienced in those early days at Washington Square? No, the re-upholsterer stuffed the seat when I had the chair recovered. I didn't request that he stuff it; he just did it. I bit my lower lip, trying to control the quivering.

"You seem to equate the height of the chairs with differences in status." Pleased with my interpretation as well as the gentle tone of my voice, I relaxed.

"Yes, I feel you're trying to be superior to your patients."

I was stung. After all, I had been furious about the chair in Joan's office at the clinic. Guilt washed over me. After a long pause I got control over myself.

"To all my patients, or to you?" I asked.

"Yes, to me, of course," she said with a clipped smile.

My neck was hot and my shoulders were tense.

"Are we competing?" I asked, with as much neutrality as I could muster.

"Yes, I guess we're competing. I don't want to feel lower. Especially because you're so much younger."

My shoulders relaxed. She seemed to understand that her feelings about the chair were more about *her* than me. She made the interpretation herself.

"I've never been in treatment with a woman before. And you seem to understand what's going on with me. It makes me feel inferior. I don't like it."

"I can understand that." I nodded my head and smiled.

She went back to the story of her father's death that she had mentioned in passing the prior week. The muscles in my lower back relaxed, the way they used to when my mother stopped yelling at me and decided to call one of her sisters. It was a reprieve.

"My father was hit by a delivery truck that went through a red light and he was thrown from the car. He was probably decapitated."

I gasped imagining her father's bloodied head flying onto the highway while his disheveled body was thrown to the side of the road. Aside from the inherent horror of what Sally was saying I was shaken by the coldness of her delivery. She went on to another topic.

"I'm really angry at Jonathan because he keeps saying my anxiety about losing my cognitive capacity is silly." Her lips pursed with annoyance.

I wanted to be soothing, but my anger at her husband for not taking her fears seriously was weighing on me.

"That must feel like he doesn't understand how frightening it is for you," I said.

Her lips relaxed. She nodded sadly. For the first time we were on the same side.

"Unfortunately, our time is up for now."

꘏꘏

I was still in a state of shock from the story of her father's bloody death when Sally left my office. She had transitioned from her father's death to talking about being disappointed that her husband wasn't more sensitive to her fears about her brain. I wondered if her anxiety about her cognitive abilities might be related to the traumas she had suffered. However, I didn't want to suggest that, because it would feel as if I was minimizing her fears. It was too early to say anything anyway because I hadn't yet formed an interpretation. When the bell rang signaling that my next patient had arrived, I was startled.

Mary Elizabeth

Mary Elizabeth walked into my office smiling and lay down on the couch without a jacket, sweater or coat covering her. It was a nasty December day, but she left her raincoat in the waiting room.

"This is the least amount of clothes I've ever worn to a session. I want to expose as much as possible to you in a way I've always avoided," she said.

A tear ran down my cheek I was glad she was on the couch and could not see it.

"I had a dream I want to tell you. I was very angry. People who lived in the apartments came out complaining the place isn't taken care of. It's dirty and falling down. Like a protest. The landlord in the dream looks like my current landlord. He's about fifty and people get quiet when he comes out. They're waiting to see what he's going to say. I step forward and yell, 'This is a disgrace. The place is falling down.'"

"Did anything happen the day or night before the dream that's related to this?" I asked.

"Yes, my landlord has been painting my apartment. He looked just like my father in the dream. My father fixed everything just like my landlord does. After I woke up I felt I was speaking out against my father. The structure is falling apart, it's crumbling. I can't keep it in any longer. It felt good. Something was collapsing that needed to come down. The facade that he kept up is coming down. My landlord has filled the cracks twice and it looked fine, but now the cracks are very pronounced and can't be plastered over any more. My father in the cellar and my landlord hammering in the basement made all the cracks come back."

"So what comes to mind about the cracks in the façade?" I asked.

"It's the lies and denial that's falling apart. I had another dream too. I was with a small child—a girl, maybe four. I was in a warehouse with her. I don't know how I got there. I went downstairs into the basement. It was an empty room and off to the side there were doors indicating other rooms. One had a window—broken, dirty and obstructed. One thing I could see though. There was a man standing facing the girl. His belt was unhooked and his zipper was down. He was holding his penis and snickering. I was terrified. The girl didn't see me. I looked for a place to hide. Then we were out on the street. The feeling was fright, mostly for the child."

I was quiet; my heart pounded.

"I've been reading this book about a woman who has an affair with her father... I can't put the book down. I read it on the subway. I was reading it in the waiting room."

"What about that?"

"When I was in the eighth grade I was going to a party at the home of a classmate. My parents knew the parents and I called home and my father was very angry at me. He wanted to control me. He conveyed the sense, 'I don't want you to have sex with another man.'"

"Another man?" I asked incredulously.

"Yes. My father used to give me these wet kisses. My mouth was wet from it. It was sexual. That's why it was easier not to have a body. In the car he'd always say, 'Close your coat' when we were driving."

"What do you make of that?" I asked. The muscles in my back were tight.

"I felt it was because my body was repulsive. He wanted me to cover it."

"And what do you think now?" My temples were pulsating.

"I think he had sexual feelings about me that he couldn't control. So he wanted me to cover up so he could control himself."

"Yes … " I held my breath.

"I had to act as if I didn't have a body so he could control himself. It makes me furious."

It was as if she had known there was something rotten but did not want to have to smell the rot and clean out the green and black mold that had been collecting for years. But she had finally decided it was time. She could bear it.

"Unfortunately, we are going to have to stop."

⟫⟪

When Mary Elizabeth walked out I was relieved that I didn't have another patient waiting. I remembered being in the car with my father; I was seven or eight years old. We were going to visit the Keffords. My crotch tingled and I felt frightened of my father. Now that I think back on it, I realize I had sexual feelings toward my father and projected them on him.

I was resisting what Mary Elizabeth and I had found. Part of me hoped Mary Elizabeth's experience of her father's sexual desire for her was a projection. I didn't want to face what had for so long been an unknown known that she had lived with in a haunted house—her father had raped her.

Sally

Despite the January weather outside, I sat in my office sweating. I was trying to relax by thinking of something amusing. My mind turned to the new series, *All in the Family*, that Stephen and I had watched the night before. The newspapers said it was the first time there was a toilet flush heard on television.

After a few minutes, I opened the door to the waiting room and invited Sally in. My back muscles tightened in expectation of her criticism. I began to understand, in a new way, why, in the early days, Joan had once forgotten our appointment and gone shopping!

I had arrived at her door for our appointment and the door was not open as it usually was. I rang the bell and there was no answer, although I heard the dog bark.

It was the session after I had ranted about her having a dog. I stood in her hall between the elevator and her apartment door. My right eye twitched as I waited, slouched against the wall.

Finally, after ten minutes, the elevator door opened, and Joan emerged with packages from Lord & Taylor.

"Oh," she said, jerking her head.

"We have an appointment at two," I said with gritted teeth.

"I'm so sorry," she said fumbling with her packages and searching for her keys.

I was quiet.

"I just need a few minutes," she said, opening the door and pointing to the open door of her office.

I entered the office and sat hunched on the couch.

Joan came in after a few minutes and said, "I'm really sorry. I just completely forgot about our appointment."

My heart palpitated and my cheeks were hot. I did not lie down on the couch. I turned to face her.

"This is about what I said about your dog, isn't it?" I asked.

She crossed and uncrossed her legs. "I think I just forgot ... I needed some things, and it was a nice day outside."

"Come on, Joan," I had yelled at her. "Let's be honest here," I said in a modulated tone. "I was in a rage about your dog and went on a rant about it."

I heaved and looked her in the eyes, silently imploring her to be straight with me.

"Okay," she said, clearing her throat. She leaned forward in her chair and said, "I think you're right. I love my dog and was upset at your rage."

Now I was the one feeling beaten up by my patient. Like Joan, I did not want to go back in the ring. After a few minutes I took a deep inhale and opened the door.

"Hello, Sally."

"You know it's really odd that your magazines are old and you cut off the address label on the magazines in the waiting room."

My jaw tightened.

"I've never seen such a thing," she said. "You must order the magazines for your house and then bring them here!" Her eyes blazed.

It was true; she was right. I couldn't block the punch. We read *The New Yorker* in our apartment before I put it in my waiting room. I was guilty and she caught me. But I didn't really understand what was unscrupulous about doing that.

"What is it about the magazines being previously read and my taking the mailing label off that is upsetting to you?" My back stiffened.

Then came a right jab.

"It means that you don't subscribe for the office, you subscribe for your house." She scowled.

She was right again. I felt a spasm of remorse, but I wasn't sure what was so depraved about it.

"What is it about that that's upsetting?" I asked in my most controlled shrink voice.

She took a breath; she was trying to figure it out. Then to my astonishment, her tone changed from outrage to amazement. Her face softened; she was no longer scandalized. I knew by then that the change in demeanor meant she had an insight about her intense reaction to me. She lay down her boxing gloves and explained it to both of us.

"My parents had a very romantic relationship," she said. "Every night they had a cocktail in the living room when my father came home from work and we weren't able to talk to them or even go in the room during cocktail hour. I think coming here feels the same to me. Your patients are secondary to your real life. We get the magazines with the label torn off. The cocktail hour is in your house."

My back relaxed and I took a deep breath. I smiled inwardly at the power of transference and wondered what she would think if she knew anything about my parents. My parents never had a cocktail together. Jews of my parents' generation and class didn't have cocktails before dinner—they had seltzer with dinner. They were from a lost civilization, like the Anasazi. The *shmata* wearing, Chinese food on Sunday, seltzer with dinner generation has died off. They were the children of European immigrants and their children prefer jeans to *shmatas*, foie gras to egg rolls and Perrier to seltzer. My mother never drank and my father only had a "seven and seven" if they had guests. My father came home at 5 p.m. and kissed my mother. He aimed for her mouth with a glimmer in his eyes, but she inevitably gave him her cheek. She never smiled at his kiss or kissed him back. She didn't ask him, "How was your day?" She ignored him and just kept on cooking and grousing about the way I set the table or the way I made the salad.

But I understood Sally's feeling because Stephen's parents had a romantic relationship that was exclusionary—that is why he did not want to wear a wedding ring like his father did. Stephen's father had graduated from NYU and was a successful businessman. Unlike my parents, Stephen's parents had a Scotch together when his father came home from work and often a glass of wine with dinner.

Feeling loving toward Sally at that moment, I knew something important was happening. Each week we went through the same cycle. She came in like Muhammad Ali, then we figured out what the criticisms meant to her and I melted. But we had not talked about what it meant that she was always denigrating me. And I didn't understand what made me feel so unhinged by her censure.

The dread of her condemnation reminded me of how I felt when my mother came home from work. There was always something I had neglected or done wrong. I buttressed myself in expectation of her yelling when I heard the front door slam. My back muscles tightened; my jaw clenched. I had cleaned the sink with Ajax, put the groceries away, set the table for dinner, made my bed, and hung up my clothes. But there was always something I forgot to do. One day she walked in the door and did not say hello, but rather headed straight to her bedroom to undress and put on her *shmata*. Then she walked into the kitchen ready to growl.

"Did you get milk while you were in the A&P?" my mother asked.

"It wasn't on the list," I said.

"I'm so tired," she said, rubbing her eyes. "Can't you look in the refrigerator? Didn't you finish the milk with your cereal this morning? Do I have to think of everything?"

"I'm sorry, Mom." I hadn't looked in the refrigerator to check. There was always something. I was always derelict.

Now, I was dreading Sally's next criticism of me. Was this my counter-transference to her? Was I experiencing her as if she were my mother? Or was she treating me the way her mother treated her? Was I feeling what she felt when she was a child? All of those things were probably happening. She was treating me the way her mother treated her and I experienced the dread and insecurity Sally must have felt as a child. But it was more intense than another analyst might have felt because it resonated with my experience of my mother.

"I'm sure it must have felt painful to see that magazine in the waiting room and feel I'm inaccessible—you're locked out of my cocktail hour and it doesn't matter what you feel or what you need."

"Yes." She sobbed.

"I think you express your disappointment and hurt as anger," I said gently. "Underneath the anger is a vulnerable little girl." I was explaining the dynamic to myself as well as to Sally. My body relaxed; I wanted to console the little girl.

"Yes." She took a tissue from the coffee table and blew her nose.

"Unfortunately, our time is up for now," I said.

⇒⇒⇒⇐⇐⇐

I sat in my chair thinking about the parallels between Sally's experience of her parents' cocktail hour and my feelings of being on the porch with the dogs barking. We both felt exiled. I wanted to hold on to that identification with her so that I could tap into it the next time she criticized me—which I knew was inevitable.

Mary Elizabeth

Mary Elizabeth walked into my office smiling and said, "It's March and it's snowing outside! That's crazy!" Then she took off her boots, painstakingly lined them up next to her and lay down on the couch. She pulled her winter coat over her, trying to cover her feet.

As I watched her struggle to cover every inch, I had an intense reaction to the return to her earlier behavior. A wave of nausea suddenly came over me. I was glad she was not facing me. My eyes were closed.

When she had her coat arranged so that only her head was visible to me, she began to talk.

"I had a dream," she said. "There was a bathroom without a door. In order to shit you had to do it in front of all these people. It wouldn't flush or I couldn't make it flush. It was a terrible mess and other people were waiting to use it. A woman from a tribe that lives in the rainforest was squatting and shitting on the floor and then she just walked away. There was shit and filth all around."

"What was the feeling in the dream?" I asked.

"Revulsion. It was disgusting." She pulled her coat up higher.

"It seems this is a common theme in your dreams. What do you think?" I asked.

"My mother was always working to keep the bathroom spotlessly clean.

We had a small bathroom that we all shared and my mother was always cleaning it. It had pink tile and fluffy pink towels. She didn't want it to look like a bathroom. It didn't look like a place where people made a mess and had diarrhea."

"What comes to mind about that?" I asked.

"There was a big sink in the basement. I feel like I'm going to vomit."

She jumped up from the couch and ran into the bathroom. I could hear her retching. I wondered if I should follow her and see if she was okay. I decided to wait; give her room to experience this. After a few minutes she came back and lay down on the couch without saying a word for a few moments. My nausea passed; I took a deep breath.

"You know one of my first images in treatment was that I was lying on the floor, like garbage, with a big pussy wound. You had long instruments with gauze at the end so you wouldn't have to come too close to examine the wounds. But it was terribly painful. God, I can feel my vagina pulsating."

Electrified by the image and stunned by her use of "pussy," I sat bolt straight in my chair. I wondered where she had picked up "pussy." She certainly didn't learn it in Catholic school. Did her father use that word?

"Do you think that's what I want—to stay away from you?" I asked.

"When I was a kid I used to have this repetitive dream that there was an evil man under the bed. If an arm or leg sticks out, he will pull me down to this dark abyss and I can't scream. People around, but I have no voice. Like Rapunzel—she better spin hay into gold or they'll take her baby away."

"Do you think you tried to make believe you were sleeping and not move when your father came into your room?"

She leaped up from the couch again and ran to the bathroom. I could hear her retching in the bathroom. I wondered to myself: *Should I ask her if she was okay or sit still?* I decided to wait for her again; give her room for this to come up—literally.

She came back, without looking at me, and lay down on the couch again. She was quiet for a few minutes.

"I feel there's something I want to vomit up, but it's not coming up," she said. Her voice was hoarse from retching.

"Yes." I whispered, as if anything louder would suppress what was coming up.

"You know when I was a child I had a repetitive dream that there were snakes crawling out from under the bed. If I kept still and kept my arms around me like this (she puts her arms around her torso) I could prevent it."

"Maybe there *was* a snake under your bed," I said.

"It sure sounds as if I knew my father was coming, doesn't it."

"Yes."

"I just can't remember it."

"Yes. Unfortunately, we're going to have to stop for now."

⟫⟪

Mary Elizabeth got up from the couch and put on her boots. She turned to me and said, "It's close now. It's almost here."

I smiled and said as gently as I could, "Yes." Like Jacques Cousteau I watched a fish deep under the ocean who had made special adaptations to living in extremely high pressure, low light conditions, filled with the deadliest of creatures. For years she had to defend herself from the viper fish, black as night with a long dorsal fin that lures the fish it preys upon, poison dart frogs and black mamba snakes.

Sally

I had been reading about the Soviets putting the first space station into orbit when the doorbell rang. I sighed deeply before I opened the door to my waiting room.

"Hello, Sally." I smiled.

"I'm depressed. I forgot to put on makeup or comb my hair before I came here.

That's very interesting. I've never done that before. I seem to want you to see me without any decoration."

She wanted me to see underneath her façade. She was sitting at the edge of the seat and had her arms around herself as if she were cold. I saw a little girl whose mother was cold and critical trying to console herself. I could identify with that.

Sally handed me the check to pay the bill for the prior month. I took the check and crossed off her name in my appointment book to indicate she paid.

"Thank you," I said.

"What are you doing that for?" Her eyes opened wide and her voice was boiling over with contempt.

"Doing what?" My right eye twitched.

"Writing down that I paid you. I've never heard of anyone doing that."

"I don't know what you mean," I said as flatly as I could. Sally reminded me of my mother. I couldn't foresee what would set her off. But I could forecast that something would.

"You're supposed to mark it down after the patient leaves." Sally said. She lifted her chin slightly and added, "Not while I'm here."

I was slugged once again; I was speechless. I never noticed what Joan did after I gave her a check because I always turned around and walked over to the couch to lie down. I was barely able to utter a response.

"What does it mean," I asked, "that I'm marking down that you paid while you're here?" I folded my hands on my lap.

"It's unprofessional; that's all," she said with raised eyebrows and nostrils flaring. "Anyway, I've been thinking about whether I want to see you or not. It's a big trip from where I live to get here."

"Do you think," I asked, sitting on my hands, "there might be something more to it?"

"Well, I liked what you said last time. It made me feel much better to think that you're not inadequate; I'm just projecting" She nodded and wrinkled her chin. "But I think I liked you better when you didn't talk. I want to know what you think, but when you tell me what you think, it's what I'd say if I were you."

"Mmm. Is that good or bad?" I asked with a smile.

"I don't know. When you were silent it gave me room for my own associations."

I was damned if I did and damned if I didn't. It was so familiar; just like home. When I gave her room for her associations she said I was cold and distant. When I changed and made more interpretations, she said she liked me better when I was silent. You're just like my mother, I thought. Whatever I do, it's not right! I thought about my unremitting anger at Joan and how hard it must have been for her to accept the battering.

"Do you think not wanting to see me might be related to my saying something that was helpful to you?" I held my breath like Houdini waiting for the stomach punch.

"Yes, I think I'm competitive with you. I want you to help me, but I don't want to feel you can help me." She raised a brow.

I nodded.

"There's something else too," she said. "My parents were contemptuous of Blacks and Jews.

My stomach tightened from the blow. Can she be antisemitic? No, I reminded myself, she told me her husband is Jewish in a previous session.

"Do you think that's related to your feelings about me?" I asked. I sat on my hands again.

"Well, you're probably Jewish," she said. She straightened up in her chair and spoke in a matter of fact tone. "And I seem to be competitive with you."

I wondered what that meant: "You're probably Jewish." Was it my nose or my Brooklyn accent or what? I didn't know if she was saying that my being Jewish made her feel superior to me. And I wasn't sure how I was going to feel if that were true.

"Can you tell me more about that?" I said, trying to be nonchalant.

"Well, I think I'm juggling feeling superior because you're Jewish with feeling inferior because you're so much younger than I am and you're helping me."

I took a deep breath and thought about what Anne would say. "She was brought up to be antisemitic and there are remnants left. That isn't her fault and, besides, that isn't the point. The issue is her rickety self-esteem."

"How does my helping you make you feel inferior?" I asked.

"If I need you then you're better than me. I want your help, but I don't want to feel helped." She rolled her eyes.

I got that. It was like those stories of people who lend money to a friend or give a needed kidney and it ends the friendship. The recipient feels angry that the benefactor was able to help them.

"Sometimes I think you're 'too nice' and not analytic enough," she said. She crossed her arms over her chest.

My back tightened. I changed my position in my chair.

"I think that *analytic* is your term for cold and uncaring." I said.

Her eyes widened; she raised her eyebrows, and she nodded her head.

"Yes, I think that's true," she said. "When you're silent and cold I feel angry at you, but have more respect for you."

My back muscles relaxed. I pondered that for a moment.

"So when you experience me as cold and silent like your mother you respect me and when you experience me as understanding and comforting you devalue me for not being as smart or competent as your mother." I nodded.

"Yes, exactly. When you're warm and understanding you're Jewish and when you're cold and silent you're a WASP. I devalue what I want." She groaned.

I laughed to myself about her stereotype of Jewish mothers as warm and understanding.

"So, you're ambivalent," I said, "about whether you want a Jewish mother or your WASP mother."

"Right," she said, wincing. "It's pretty stupid."

"No, it's not stupid. It's actually perfectly understandable considering the way you were brought up."

I'd taken a long drive in terrible traffic and finally arrived at the beach to find a full moon lighting up the ocean.

"We're going to have to stop for now."

>>>.<<<

As I watched Sally leave, I exhaled deeply. I was proud that for the first time in her life, despite all the prior analysis she had, she was understanding herself in a new way. I smiled, feeling a surge of admiration for her. She was brutally honest with herself as well as with me and it seemed that an alternative way of treating herself was emerging. She had always treated herself the way her mother had treated her, and now there was the possibility of offering herself some comfort—some chicken soup.

Mary Elizabeth

Mary Elizabeth was ten minutes late for her session. I sat reading "A Mother's Plea." It was a *Times* story about a Russian-Jewish woman who was allowed to leave Russia and emigrate to Israel, but the Soviets wouldn't let her 23-year-old daughter leave with her. I alternated between despair about the Soviet-Jewish plight and concern that Mary Elizabeth might have been so depressed that she stayed in bed. When she walked into my office she said, "I didn't want to come." Then she carefully took off her shoes, lined them up, and arranged herself on the couch, pulling her spring coat over her.

"When I was walking from the train I had this image of being locked in the basement and my mother finally opens the door. I'm so happy. I go running up to her, but then I'm furious at her. I'm enraged. I have this incredible love and desire and utter total rage."

"And that's how you feel about me?" I asked. I shifted in my chair.

"Yes. You know over the weekend I go into this frozen state. I can't think or move. It's a state of no-sense. I can go without eating or drinking for two days or more when I'm in that frozen state. I had a dream last night. I was in a room and I might have been in a bed asleep. I awakened and there was a large bear in the room. I got out of the room and into the room next door. There was a young person coming down the hallway and I was trying to signal her to come to me instead of the room with the bear."

"What was the main feeling in the dream?" I asked.

"I was frightened and desperate to save the young person from the bear." She wrapped her arms around her torso.

"Does anything come to mind about a bear?" I leaned forward.

"When I was little, I used to have a repetitive dream about bears. The light is on in my parents' bedroom and I'm sitting in the bed with them. I look up and there's a bear putting his paw through the window. I'm terrified and they don't see it. I look outside and there are all these bears out there. I see the danger, but they don't see it."

"What comes to mind about that?" I asked.

"The bear can be a dancing bear. It can be fun, but it can be terrifying." She crossed her arms.

"What about somebody who you'd like to play with, but is sometimes ferocious?"

"It's my father." She got up quickly from the couch and ran into the bathroom. I could hear her retching. In a few minutes she came back, without looking at me, and lay down on the couch again. I could see drops of sweat on her neck. She took a tissue from the table and wiped her neck.

Silently, I waited for her reaction.

She began to sob violently. Her body was vibrating on the couch. I could barely understand her through the sobs.

"I think the little girl I was trying to save was me. I hate myself. When I heard the door squeak at night, I knew he was coming for one of us. But I didn't know which one. I didn't want it to be me."

Her sobbing was so intense I couldn't comprehend her words for a minute. Then she calmed down enough for me to understand what she was saying.

"I would try to be frozen, stop breathing. I thought if I was frozen he'd take my sister instead of me".

She was sobbing so hard her body was pulsating.

"I didn't protect her. I didn't want to protect her. I just didn't want him to take me ..."

I waited. I didn't want to interrupt the process. She was finally getting it out. I wanted to give her the space to finally spew it up.

"Of course."

"I hate myself. I didn't protect her."

"You couldn't protect her," I said, leaning forward in my chair, "you were a victim yourself."

"I could have told my mother," she said. Tears flowed down the side of her face.

"What do you imagine she would have done?" Her mother would not have done anything, I thought. She probably would have yelled at her. Or is that my mother?

"The truth is she knew. It was impossible not to know. We were living in this little house. The stairs creaked. She had to know what was going on when he got out of bed and she heard the stairs creak. She didn't want to have sex with him. She was afraid of having any more babies—or miscarriages. She knew that, so there was no point in telling her. She would just get furious and tell me I was crazy."

Mary Elizabeth stopped talking for a minute.

"Can you tell me what you're feeling?" I asked.

"I feel calm. I've been choking on this for so long. It's finally out."

"Yes."

She was sobbing heavily. Her words were barely understandable.

"That's why I didn't want to have a body. That's why I wanted to cover it up."

"Yes." I wiped my cheek.

She was quiet, but the sobbing had subsided and she was breathing normally.

She was hugging herself.

As softly as I could I said, "We're going to have to stop for now."

➤➤➤◄◄◄

Mary Elizabeth got up from the couch and put on her shoes. She turned to face me and said, "I love you. Thank you." I smiled and said, "You're welcome." I wanted to say: "I love you too." But I had learned why it was important to maintain clear limits.

Paris

On our first day in Paris, Stephen and I watched a woman with a long Gallic nose sniff the fruit in her crocheted grocery bag while a young Moroccan-looking girl with frizzy black hair counted her change. We had walked from St. Germaine to Montparnasse to get the train for the twenty-minute trip to Versailles. Celebrating our first anniversary and delayed honeymoon, we felt so lucky to be in Paris on a sunny day at the end of July, that we practically skipped on the street. Tears welled up in my eyes as Stephen took my hand and guided me across the boulevard.

When we arrived at the Versailles station and walked toward the chateau, I read the sign on the front of a laundromat out loud: *"Libre service laverie."*

"How come the laundromat is free?" I asked him, expecting him to know the answer to all my queries regarding the quirks of French culture.

He chuckled. "What grade did you get in French? It means 'self-service' not 'free.'"

"I got a 65 and that was just because the teacher liked me," I giggled. "How far is it to the chateau?"

He was being playful. *"Où est le château?_*Why did they build the chateau so far from the train?" Leaning over, he kissed my ear.

Stephen was so relaxed in Paris. We were staying at the Hotel Lenox on Rue Université in a room that had a clear view of the roof of the building next door. There was barely space to walk around the bed, but it was Paris. The creaky elevator landed on each floor with a loud thump that left you shaking, but it felt charming rather than frightening.

The second day we took the Metro to République and walked down the Rue de Fauborg du Temple to the St. Martin Canal and watched the bridge open at Rue Dieu. Like children we gasped with pleasure as the swing bridge opened to allow a barge to pass. We ran along the side of the canal as the water lowered under the barge and filled the next lock—a giant bathtub. When the barge passed out of our sight, we sat on a bench and Stephen pulled my legs over his lap. We snuggled for a while, and then walked aimlessly until we found a café that seemed suitable for lunch. We both had *oeufs en meurette*. It's such a simple dish, just eggs poached in red wine, and yet it's so intense; we lapped it up with a fresh baguette and felt as guilty as if we had indulged in a plate of foie gras.

The third day we walked to Père Lachaise and mapped out a walking tour of the graves. Stephen chose Edith Piaf and Oscar Wilde, while I chose Isadora Duncan and Marcel Proust. I chose Proust because I had studied *Swann's Way* during college; I chose Isadora Duncan because I learned about her during college, but not in a class.

Judd Boynton, a retired architect, hired me to type his narrated family history because he wanted his children to know their ancestry. I'd never known anyone whose family hadn't arrived at Ellis Island from Poland or Russia or Italy in the early 1900's. His ancestors arrived on the Mayflower. So many generations of Boyntons had lived in Berkeley that there were streets named after them. Each time we drove up to his house in the hills above Berkeley and looked out the floor-to-ceiling windows to the Bay Bridge, he brought out cheese and crackers and told me stories about his infamous cousin Isadora Duncan. I was enchanted. He explained how she had been strangled by one of her scarves when it was caught in the tire of her lover's sports car. It wasn't Paris Singer's car, Judd was careful to explain. The son of Isaac Singer, the founder of the sewing machine, was one of Isadora's lovers, but not the one responsible for her death.

Now, we looked for Oscar Wilde's grave. It was easy to find because, even on a weekday, there was a crowd around the Egyptian-style sculpture that marks his grave, and women were still kissing it and leaving lipstick marks. We were both appalled when we saw the penis had been broken off the anatomically correct male body.

"I guess one of his fans wanted something to hold onto," Stephen said in between snickers.

When we found Edith Piaf's grave we found some adoring fans had gathered there to lay red roses, but poor Marcel Proust was alone. I was surprised to find out he was Jewish; it made me feel a kinship with him. Stephen leaned over to kiss me ever so lightly on my cheek and read:

"Let us be grateful to people who make us happy: They are the charming gardeners who make our souls. Ah, Proust."

No one was around so I put my arms around Stephen, kissed the dimple next to his earlobe and stroked the three new gray hairs that had emerged just above his ear. Then I turned his face toward me, looked directly at his greenish hazel eyes, and said, "I love you."

He smiled, lifted me, holding me tightly, and kissed me deeply. Then he gently returned me to the ground and gave me the tiniest of kisses on my cheek.

September 11, 1971

When I arrived at Joan's there was construction going on. The elevator I had usually taken was being worked on, so I had to take the service elevator. I asked the doorman what was happening and he said they were making the elevator self-service and doing some redecorating.

"What will John do then?" I asked naively.

"He's retiring. He was over seventy."

Sad I had not said goodbye to him, I frowned. I had seen him three times a week for years and had just taken him for granted. I guess, I thought he would always be there.

When I rang Joan's bell, she startled me by opening the door herself rather than ringing me in. Her face was ashen as if all the color had been siphoned out and her eyes had small dark pouches under them. I had a feeling of foreboding; I could hear my heart pounding.

"Hi, Rose," she said with as much of a smile as she could muster.

She opened the door to her office for me to go in, and when she walked over to her chair she was limping. I didn't notice it before because she was sitting in her chair the last couple of times I arrived for my sessions. I wondered what that could be about. Maybe she hurt her leg or needed a hip replacement.

She said, "Instead of lying down today, why don't you sit up?"

Then I knew this wasn't about her leg or her hip. Propping up the pillow against the wall under the Georgia O'Keeffe poster, I tried not to breathe, as if that would delay the bad news. I noticed the philodendrons by the window were brown around the edges; she must have forgotten to water them.

"I thought I hurt myself exercising at the gym when I first felt a pain in my side." Her tone was calm and accepting; I could feel myself exhale. Her gray roots were showing and her hair was flat on one side as if she had slept on that side and not taken a shower and washed her hair that morning.

"When it didn't get any better in a few weeks I went to the doctor and he said it was probably a hairline fracture. He took an X-ray. Then he called me to tell me it wasn't a hairline fracture—the cancer has returned. It's metastasized and it's cracked my bones in the hip and pelvis."

I let out a gasp. "Oh, fuck!" My lower back tightened.

She went on unruffled. "I'm going to need a partial hip replacement and they're going to put a pin in my hip. I won't be able to walk for several weeks."

"Will you come back after that?" I asked hopefully, like a child asking her mother if she will come home after she goes away for a trip.

She looked down for a moment as if she were avoiding my eyes. Still not looking at me, she said hesitantly, "No ... I won't be coming back. It's terminal." Then she looked at me and her eyes were wet with tears. Her shoulders were hunched as if she had given up on trying to sit up straight.

I struggled for breath as a waterfall of tears careened off my face. "How will I go on without you?"

I got off the couch and kneeled in front of her chair, putting my head on her lap and my arms around her. I was quiet; I just wanted to hold onto her.

She stroked my hair and whispered, "You will be fine. You've come such a long way, you're such a good analyst and you have Stephen. You'll be okay."

"Joan, I love you true and blue and like glue. I hope you know that."

"Of course, I do."

I noticed a run in her stocking and suddenly realized I might be hurting her by leaning on her that way, so I got up and walked over to sit on the couch.

I wondered if Joan felt guilty leaving me in the middle. The problem is you never know what's the middle.

I pondered the question out loud to Joan. "Maybe that's why sessions are purposely set up to end at an arbitrary moment—to end in the middle."

"What do you mean?" The lines around Joan's eyes had deepened considerably from the last time I'd looked at her face closely.

"Well they always end after 45 minutes no matter what's going on in the session. I used to get so angry at you for that. It felt so heartless. It felt like you didn't care about me."

Joan laughed and said, "Yes, I remember." Then she added, more seriously, "There are things you can't control. We have to live with that." Her arms were crossed as if she were hugging herself.

"But you seem so calm. You don't sound angry. Why?"

"Well, you know ... Of course, you *don't* know, but my mother died of breast cancer when I was sixteen," she said, knitting her brows. "I think I've always known this was going to happen. It's been a time bomb ticking my whole life. It isn't a surprise."

I was torn between the pleasure at her telling me about herself and my compassion for her having spent her whole life waiting to die.

"How were you able to stand my anger at my mother when you lost yours at such a young age?" I asked.

She tilted her head as if she was considering the question, but then her face grimaced in pain when she tried shifting her body in her chair. "My mother never talked to me about her illness or about dying. My father died when I was ten and there was never any discussion about it. My mother would say, 'He's dead, what's there to talk about.' And when she was dying, she never tried to help me and my brother work through the loss of her. She didn't want to talk about it. So I understood your anger at your mother."

"So, you were angry at your mother too," I said with raised eyebrows.

"Yes. Maybe that's why your analysis has worked so well. I've always identified with you. Even rooted for you. My mother used to say: 'You'll break your arm patting yourself on the back.' So, it's been a struggle for me to feel pleasure at my accomplishments, but it's been a delight to see yours. I feel so proud of you."

She smiled at me again, but her eyes looked sad. "I'm afraid we're going to have to stop now."

An old part of me erupted for a moment—I bawled. "You mean stop forever?"

"Yes."

The eruption was over in a moment. I didn't want to cause her any more pain than she was already suffering from.

"Can I visit you?" I pleaded.

"I don't know yet. We'll have to see. Do you think you can bear that?"

"I don't know. I guess I'll have to."

"Why don't you wait a month so I can see how I am doing after the surgery and when I start the chemo. Then I'll know better."

"Okay." I got up from the couch and looked into her sad blue eyes and said in a choking voice, "Goodbye. Please remember I love you true and blue." Then I turned and walked out the door of the office.

⟫⟪

I contained myself until I reached the street. Weeping turned into bawling by the time I got to Broadway. People turned to look, but kept their distance, walking past me quickly as if they would catch whatever I had. I thought about what I said to her. By then I knew I didn't need to see Joan in order to ward off my sense of isolation and exile. I had Stephen and a growing practice and I was feeling full and capable of nurturing. Joan and I had been talking about terminating my treatment soon anyway. I wanted to see her because I cared about her; I wanted to give her my love, but I had stopped feeling desperate for her.

I thought about Frume Minkowitz and my guilt when I had to leave her in the middle of the semester. One day I walked out of my classroom at Brooklyn College and a young woman was standing in the hall with a baby in a snuggly on her chest and two toddlers holding her hands. She was wearing a *sheitel* and a long-sleeve blouse although it was a warm spring day. She looked familiar, but I didn't know who she was.

"Rose?" Her large brown eyes looked intensely into mine, "I'm Frume."

She had come to tell me she had not only survived the aftermath of my leaving her, but she had thrived. Her smile was radiant as she introduced her three children.

279

She said, "I'd like you to meet my children. This is Avram, he's three." She raised her right hand to indicate the little boy with *peyos* was Avram. Then she raised her left hand to indicate the four- or five-year-old with the long pink dress and matching tights and said, "And this is Shoshanna." She looked down at the sleeping baby in the snuggly and said, "And last but not least, this is Joshua."

"Oh, my god," I gasped and immediately felt embarrassed at the inappropriateness of using G-d's name in response to her.

"I wanted you to know," she said with a knowing smile, "that you changed my life and I never forgot you. I had a rough patch for a while but now I have Shmule and our children and I'm very happy. I wanted you to know that." A tear ran down her left cheek.

Part III

ENDINGS

Visiting My Mother

My mother and I walked a block from her private nursing home, Harbor House, toward the deli to get her favorite chocolate ice cream. But she said her legs felt weak and she couldn't go on, so I left her sitting on a bench and hurried back to get my car. It was a glorious October afternoon and she enjoyed the warmth of the sun on her face. When I returned to get her, she smiled and said, "It's nice to be outside."

Fumbling with her seatbelt, her shallow breath warmed my neck as I tried to insert the belt in the buckle. My lower back ached and I smiled to myself thinking, "That's where the saying 'pain in the ass' comes from." We drove one block to the deli and I double parked. I held on to her upper arm as she tried to get out of the car. But she couldn't quite pry herself out so I put my arms around her emaciated body and lifted her. My blouse was wet from the exertion. Her wrinkled skin hung under her upper arms and I inhaled the odor of old age.

It reminded me of visiting my paternal grandmother when I was a child. My mother never wanted to take the ride to Brighton Beach to visit her, but my father insisted that I join him. He tried to entice me with the promise of Mrs. Stahl's knishes on the way home—and that was tempting—but still I never went willingly. I don't remember calling her "Grandma." I don't know what I called her. I just remember the acrid smell of her skin that permeated her clothes.

I took my mother's arthritic hand, guiding her into the store, and found a chair for her to sit on while I parked the car. "I'll be right back Mom," I reassured her, but I didn't know if she took it in. I was concerned that she would get frightened if she suddenly felt alone in a strange place. As I hurried out of the store, she stared vacantly at the young Korean woman at the cash register.

When I returned, I was relieved to see my mother was not frightened. She was gazing into space, oblivious to the firemen with yellow rubber pants up to their thighs who were searching for salsa and chips to take back to the firehouse. She paid no attention to the obese meter maid who bought coffee and put four sugars in it. She was unfazed by the M&Ms package a teenager had mindlessly dropped on the floor. She didn't even notice the cockroach that climbed the wall next to her chair. This was the same woman who washed the Formica counters with Ajax several times each day and once ran out of a restaurant after we had ordered our food because she saw a cockroach. Now she was blank, as the bug crossed directly in her line of vision.

But she lit up when I said, "Let's get some chocolate ice cream." She followed me around as I searched for the freezer, but she didn't know who I was. When I finally found a chocolate popsicle with dark chocolate coating, I carefully took off the wrapper, got a napkin to put around the stick and handed it to her. We walked outside so she could sit in the sun and eat it. I watched a smile come across her face as the ice cream dripped on her blouse. My tears welled up; I wanted her to enjoy the ice cream.

My mother had never enjoyed buying me ice cream—she glared whenever she handed the coins to Joe, the old Italian man who pushed his cart along Webster Avenue every day during the summer. And she never joined me—it was not an opportunity for sharing a moment of contentment. It was an obligation, like buying notebooks for school, that she was willing to fulfill, but gave her no satisfaction. Probably her mother had never shared any pleasurable moments with her, so she had no model for nurturing.

When my mother was young her mother was overwhelmed with anxiety and worry because she had an asthmatic husband who couldn't work and five children to support. He had been a successful fur trader in Kiev and did not immigrate because of the pogroms following the assassination of Alexander II or the conscription of young Jewish men into the Russian army for twenty years. Rather he and his young wife came to the United States because they thought the weather would be better for his health. He couldn't stand the muggy summers with daily showers and he couldn't breathe outside during the sub-zero winters. When they moved to New York, they did not settle in the overpopulated slum-ghetto on the Lower East Side, but rather in Brownsville, Brooklyn near Sutter Avenue. Although my grandfather spoke Russian as well as Yiddish, he did not speak English, so his employment prospects were limited—he got a job as a house painter. They were surprised when his breathing got worse. Sadly, they never figured out that years of being around furs dyed with paraphenylene diamine (PPD) had caused occupational asthma, and melamine and epoxy-based paint were the worst possible irritants to his lungs.

By the time my mother and I returned from the deli to Harbor House, I was eager to leave—I was exhausted. We walked into the lounge decorated with glass chandeliers and long tables where the residents sat facing the front of the room while their aides stood around chatting in Russian. Mary, the one Black resident, was calmly talking to herself, while the white woman next to her kept yelling, "Help me, help me." Occasionally, her aide would turn to her and say, "Dorothy, calm down now." But Dorothy continued unabated. My mother took her usual seat between Millie (who was 90 and used a walker, but was still lucid) and Fritzi (who was perfectly mobile, but insisted I was her sister Dotty). Millie whispered to me, "Fritzi is really out of it." I smiled in confirmation, told them all I had to leave, and kissed my mother's parched cheek.

As soon as I got on the Belt Parkway, the traffic was backed up and I sat there for twenty minutes, intermittently sniffing my arm to assure myself I didn't smell old. When the cars finally started moving, a red Volkswagen cut me off and the driver gave me the finger as he passed me. Then I hit traffic again going over the Brooklyn Bridge. Driving home took over an hour and a half instead of the usual half hour.

I stopped in my office to check my messages. Turning on the radio when I entered my waiting room, I was glad WQXR had Horowitz playing Scarlatti, and then I went into the office and stretched out on my analytic couch. Taking time out to unwind before checking my messages gave me a twinge of guilt, but I decided to bear it rather than relinquish the pleasure. Lifting my legs made the muscles in my back ache and I let out an involuntary "Oy." I smiled at myself—still a kid from Brooklyn.

I thought again about my maternal grandmother. She died when I was eight years old—I had only known her as an old woman with gray hair and a black dress who put her teeth in a glass a night. I had never talked to her about life in Kiev or what it had been like to be widowed in her forties; I did not remember ever having a conversation with her.

After a few minutes, I was calm enough to listen to the messages. There were two; the first one was from Harbor House. It was the familiar voice of Frances, the receptionist: "We can't find your mother's doctor and she needs new prescriptions. He seems to have retired and Dr. Lee says he's no longer your mother's doctor." Curses flew out of me. I was just there! I knew her old doctor retired. I had found her a new doctor—Dr. Lee; I loved him. He answered phone calls and talked to me like I was an adult. I didn't want to lose him and go looking for another doctor.

I called him immediately and left a message and remarkably, within five minutes, I heard his voice on the phone. I pleaded with him, like a little girl pulling on his pant leg, without even letting him utter a word beyond identifying himself.

"Dr. Lee, why don't you want to be my mother's doctor?"

"No, that's not true. Harbor House told me she has another doctor," he said.

Oh, I thought, I've already gone through this with them. Why doesn't Frances write it down? Her husband is sick and she's totally distracted. My mother's old doctor retired—Dr. Lee is her doctor.

"They're all confused. You're her doctor." I banged my fist on the arm of the chair.

"Oh," he said, "that's fine—no problem."

I wasn't going to let my mother die any more miserably than nature determined. I knew I couldn't stop the mini-strokes that were taking away more and more of her cognition; she couldn't recognize playing cards or bathe herself. I couldn't stop the macular degeneration that was taking away more of her vision each week. I couldn't stop the dying. But at least I could make sure she was supervised so that she took her medication, ate three meals a day, had her clothes cleaned and had a shower. I could visit her each week and make sure she got the care she needed. I could do that.

My foot was throbbing because my toe had torn through my pantyhose and was hitting my shoe. I gathered up my jacket, purse and briefcase, grabbed the knob of the door and swung it open, but it slammed back, catching my ring in the deadbolt cylinder. I dropped everything in a spasm of agony and dislodged my pulsating finger from the door. I dissolved into a sobbing heap on the hall floor amidst my coat, purse and all of the contents of my briefcase that were strewn around me. I wailed in pain and then moaned like a wounded animal that had been run over, but was not dead. "It's not fair, it's not fair ..." I moaned. I sat there until the sobs turned to sniffles. My finger was swollen to twice its size and had already turned black and blue—my ring was cutting off the circulation. "Shit," I thought as I started hyperventilating, "they're going to have to cut my finger off." I winced, imagining my hand with a stump where my ring finger used to be. I managed to get up and open the door to my office, remove ice from the freezer and put it in a plastic bag. "Don't be silly," I told myself as I slid down the wall and sat on the kitchen floor, "they won't cut off the finger, they'll just cut off the ring." After a few minutes of icy numbness, I went out to the hall and picked up all the things I'd left in a heap, put them inside my office, and headed for the elevator.

As I approached our apartment, my finger pulsated and my stomach was churning. I imagined opening the door and feeling the warmth of the oven and the smell of a chicken roasting. I turned the key and sobbed as the air, redolent with caramelized garlic, greeted me.

Visiting Joan

I looked down at the dahlias I'd brought—some white dinner plates and some blue cactus. I had grown them at the weekend house in Connecticut that Stephen and I bought when I finished my dissertation and got promoted to Assistant Professor at Brooklyn College. It was a small house in disrepair, but it had enough land for a garden. I had planted the dahlia tubers in June, and they were still in bloom, although it was early December, because there had not been a serious frost yet.

I loved the way I arranged them for Joan. I had been studying flower arranging—I bought books about it and practiced positioning flowers in vases of different colors and sizes. The dahlias looked sculpted in contrast to the rag-tag way I used to arrange them. You have to choose a vase that's just the right size and shape. Now I understood. Part of the pleasure was that it was so alien to me—so "not me." One of my patients once commented that she was surprised I wore red nail polish—she said it was so "not you."

My mother wore big bloomers with holes and stains—she never had fresh flowers in the house, only plastic ones that gathered dust. She was an anti-aesthete, not interested in considerations of beauty—only functionality. On Webster Avenue the back "garden" was an area large enough for a shade garden around the perimeter and grass in the middle where we could have put out chairs. The view to the north was the elevated train that made the house shake when it roared to a stop at EighteenthAvenue; the view to the east was the alley behind the Culver movie theatre; and on the west side was somebody's garage. My parents could have planted clematis or something to block out the view and make it feel cozy. But they didn't—the idea of making the yard beautiful never occurred to them. It was just a plot of dirt with underpants swinging from the clothes line strung over it.

Not interested in looking at beautiful things, my mother was only interested in how they looked in the eyes of others. She displayed cut crystal vases everywhere in our house, but no flowers. Thinking back, that might have been cultural rather than personal—I read somewhere that there are many words for a dope in Yiddish (schlemiel, schmuck, shlump, shmoe, putze, etc.), but only two for flowers.

In college I took a personality inventory and ranked below average on "the importance of physical surroundings." I was oblivious—but not like my mother. She was focused on what her sister Gus would think. I, on the other hand, had been so obsessed with what was going on *inside* me, I didn't pay much attention to my physical surroundings. I wanted my apartment to be clean and orderly, but I dismissed beautiful objects as *tchochekes*.

Stephen grew up dining with Gorham silverware; eating off the "good china" every day; and using linen napkins. Joan and I never explicitly talked about it. But the more I worked out my inner demons with her (or rather the more I *acted them out* on her), the more space there was for fully experiencing the pleasures of life and the more determined I was to enjoy them.

I had not seen Joan since our final session three months ago and I was glad she was allowing me to visit. When I rang the bell, I fumbled with the vase, expecting to have to open the door myself. I guess part of me was expecting, or maybe just hoping, Joan would buzz me in from her office. My head was pounding and the muscles in my lower back were tight. I wondered what Joan was going to look like. Would she be bald? Would she look skinny and dried up? Would her skin be red and blotchy?

I was startled when the door opened and the Latina housekeeper greeted me. The black Labrador jumped up and barked. My heart palpitated, but she held the leash tightly and yelled, "Buster, stop."

Turning to me, she smiled and said in heavily accented English, "Hello, you must be Rose. Joan is expecting you. I'm Maria."

"Hello, I'm glad to meet you, Maria." I smiled, grateful that her fleshy arms were holding the leash securely.

Maria commented on the beautiful flowers and indicated that I should follow her. The doors from the waiting room to the kitchen and the rest of the apartment were open. I had yearned to go through those doors—to be allowed into her life. Now I was being invited to cross over the line that had been forbidden. I held my breath as I walked into her bedroom, trying to control the jumble of anxiety and excitement.

Joan was lying down. It was a spacious room with a high ceiling and a yellow-green molding framing the pale yellow walls. She gasped with pleasure when she saw the flowers.

"Are those from your garden? Did you pick them for me? They're so beautiful."

I walked over to the table to put down the vase and said, "Yes, I have a whole field of them in Connecticut. It's great; they're bulbs and come back every year."

She was wearing a pink cotton nightgown, her hair was thinning, and she had no makeup on. I could see the creases in her cheeks from all those years of smiling empathically. When she saw me, she put out her arms to indicate I should come over and hug her. I had wanted to embrace her so many times over the years, and now she was finally inviting me to, but I was going to lose her shortly. My mother never encouraged me to embrace her; she allowed it. There was no mutual pleasure or intimacy—she simply consented to my need to express my love for her.

Maria set up the walker next to the bed and Joan grimaced in pain as she pulled her legs around to the edge of the bed. Then Maria helped her put on her terry cloth robe and when she got herself set on the walker, she turned to me and said, "The chemo hasn't made me sick yet so why don't we go into the kitchen and have some lunch. Tomorrow I'll probably be too sick to eat." For years I had ached to have lunch with her, to sit at her kitchen table, have a two-way conversation, and not have to leave after 45 minutes. Maria helped Joan get from the walker to a chair at the kitchen table. But then she had to take the dog out for a walk so I was happily left alone with Joan.

"There's bread on the counter," she said

I smelled the fresh rye bread and thought about the sandwiches I used to eat at Linda's house—rare, paper-thin roast beef from the Jewish delicatessen.

"And there's turkey and roast beef in the refrigerator," Joan continued. "Do you like mustard or mayo?"

She knew my most intimate fantasies, but she didn't know the most mundane details about me.

"What would *you* like? Roast beef or turkey, mayo or mustard?" I held my breath, as if we were in a session, unsure if I'd succeeded in asking the question so casually that she might actually answer. To here

"I'd like the roast beef and the mayo. Thanks."

She wasn't going to ask me: "What does that make you think of?" or "What comes to mind about roast beef and mayo?"

"What do you want to drink?" I asked.

"Milk would be good," she said looking up at me with a smile.

292

I started to laugh. "Milk and roast beef? I always knew you were a weird kind of Jew. What kind of Jew drinks milk with a roast beef sandwich?"

She made an exaggerated pout and said, "You know I'm not much of a Jew."

Her wrinkles stood out on her swollen face.

"You're mixing meat and dairy," I said. "That's not kosher."

"My parents were Jews in name only. They left the Bronx and moved to the Jersey suburbs. We didn't have a kosher house. We always had milk with roast beef sandwiches."

"Ugh," I uttered in mock disgust. I smiled to myself thinking about Stephen's love of a strawberry malted with a cheeseburger. We were both silent for a moment, enjoying our banter. I was doing something forbidden and she was joining me.

"What about egg creams?" she asked. "Don't you love a chocolate egg cream with a roast beef sandwich?"

"I love chocolate egg creams, but I wouldn't have one with a roast beef sandwich." I acted outraged at the suggestion.

"Well luckily I'm not your mother's daughter."

"Yes, good point!" We both giggled.

I put the glass of milk and sandwich on the table in front of Joan and sat down across from her, feeling guilty that I was so happy.

The Last Mile

Stephen had been promoted to the head of the New York office of his public relations firm and was earning more than my salary at Brooklyn College and my therapy income combined. So, when my mother's funds had run out at the end of October 1971, he agreed that we could afford to pay the monthly fee for Harbor House and some extra money for a part-time aide, Galena, to look in on her each day. A recent immigrant from the Soviet Union, Galena had worked in a hospital in Moscow and now worked full-time at the facility. She made extra money looking in on some of the patients. Straining to cover the costs for four months, I was furious when I visited several times and found my mother sleeping in her room in the afternoon while other residents were outside in the garden or listening to music. I visited the Hebrew Home in Riverdale several times and thought the care would be better and the cost would be covered by Medicaid.

I dreaded explaining to my mother that we could no longer afford Harbor House. My mother's dementia had at first improved her disposition, but now she was increasingly hostile. I knew she wouldn't comprehend what was happening to her and I did not want her to yell at me and make me feel guilty. When the day to move her to the Hebrew Home arrived, I had not talked to her about it. I found her in her room. It was spacious with good light and a commanding view of Sheepshead Bay, but she never opened the blinds to look at the sunset or the fishing boats on the water. She didn't sit at the round oak table in her room or water the orchids and African violets I had brought for her window sill. They sat in their pots, brown leaves crumpled in the dirt.

So, I decided to tell her we were going for a ride and break the news that she was moving to a nursing home when we were on our way. I knew she would be upset, but I was trying to steel myself.

Feeling guilty that I was letting her leave without saying good-bye to Galena, who I had told the previous week, I changed my plan. Galena came from a culture in which caring for elders was an unquestioned obligation. The prior week she had glared at me critically and said, "She won't last if you take her away from me." She was probably speaking from the vantage point of someone about to lose some helpful additional income, but nonetheless her words stung. So against my better judgment, I said, "Mom, we're going for a ride, do you want to give Galena a hug?"

Even with dementia, my mother could sense that something was awry. She knew we weren't going to the deli for ice cream. She didn't want to go; she refused. So, there we were standing in front of Harbor House on a bitter cold February day—my mother looking at me as if I were a total stranger who was trying to abduct her. "Go to hell, I'm not going anywhere," she shouted as she held on to Galena's arm. Galena put her arm around my mother and kissed her on the cheek.

Feeling like an abuser, I imagined old women with their walkers and their Russian and Caribbean aides lined up in the lobby whispering to each other: "Look at what that bitch is doing to her mother." "Isn't it terrible?" and "What a shame!" Part of me wanted to grab my mother's skinny arm and push her into the car, but I controlled myself. Instead, I spoke in my calm, controlled therapist's voice.

"Mom, we have to leave," I said. "You need a lot of help and you can't get it here. You need to be at a place with doctors and nurses on staff. You need a place where people make sure you eat properly, get exercise, and the medical care you need."

"Go to hell. I'm not getting in that car."

I tried reasoning with her in an attempt to offset feeling like the abuser I imagined the people passing by on the street were whispering to each other about. "Mom, the new place is beautiful, it's like a park on the Hudson River, and they will take care of you better." She was unmoved. Finally, I blurted out, "Mom the other place is free!"

She stared at me, her eyes bulging. "Who are you? I'm not going with you!"

"Mom," I pleaded, "this is Vladimir." I pointed to the heavy set, fiftyish, Russian man with tussled gray hair that I had hired to drive my mother and me to the Hebrew Home in Riverdale. He was sitting at the wheel of a large black Chrysler, wearing a dark crumpled suit and a white polyester shirt with a wide collar that was only partly inside his jacket. "Mom, Vladimir is my friend."

"He's old enough to be my father! I'm not going with him." My mother shouted and grabbed Galena more tightly.

I laughed but tried to stifle it. I looked at Vladimir to see how he was reacting to the insult. The top button of his shirt was open and his tie was knotted two or three inches below the first fold in his neck. He was sweating profusely despite the cold weather; I could see a bead of sweat, like a tear, rolling down the side of his face. I imagined his feelings were hurt. But then I realized he didn't hear what my mother had said—he just wanted her to get in the car so he could start moving. He looked silently at his fake Rolex as if checking the time would make it go faster.

Galena smirked and said to Vladimir, "*Razvye eto nye oozhasno?*" He laughed in seeming agreement. I didn't understand, but I imagined she had said, "Isn't this horrible?"

I wanted to get the dirty deed over with. "Mom, Vladimir is waiting for us."

"Sure," she said in cocky tone, "but I'm not going with him. Go to hell."

I looked at this demented woman. This was the same mother who screamed and yelled at me so much when I was a child that I felt sure I couldn't do anything right—the mother who had provoked fear and anxiety in me my whole life. But she had never cursed. This was a new level of aggression.

My mother turned to Galena, who looked uncomfortable and glum despite her robust pink cheeks, and said, "Are you coming with me?"

Galena was torn: if she told my mother "no," my mother wouldn't get in the car and I would be angry. But she didn't want to lie to my mother either. Her blue eyes looked up at the sky as if God would offer the answer to the conundrum.

I checked my watch. We were supposed to be at the Hebrew Home at two o'clock and it was getting late. I imagined finally getting my mother there and a smiling intake nurse saying, "Sorry, it's too late. You'll have to bring her back tomorrow."

I was stuck; I didn't know how to get my mother into the car. It was freezing and we were at a standoff. My head was pounding. Finally, after what seemed like an hour, I said, "Galena has to ask Rita for permission to come with us. Why don't you get in the car and she'll ask permission?" I lied to my mother. Galena wasn't going to ask permission. I didn't want her to come. If she did we would have to repeat this whole scene at the Hebrew Home and I would have to drive Galena back to Sheepshead Bay and listen to her tell me what a horrible daughter I was. Ever since I had told her what I was going to do, she had taken every opportunity to tell me that my mother wouldn't eat or allow anyone else but her to take care of her.

"Why don't you help my mother to the car?" I beseeched her as I stepped back.

She obediently walked my mother to the car and opened the door with her left hand, holding my mother's arm with her right hand. My mother complied and got into the car; I put the seat belt around her and buckled it. She didn't fight back. I breathed a sigh of relief, closed the door and went around to the other side. I knew she was furious, but I didn't know what else to do. I had to get her to Riverdale. "Bye Galena," I waved to her. She muttered something in Russian, "*Eta staraya lyedi sobirayetsya bit' myertvoy chyeryez myesyats.*" I did not know what it meant, but I suspected she was saying: "Just wait, you bitch, she'll be dead in a month."

"Please put on some music for her," I told Vladimir. I imagined classical or maybe Frank Sinatra, but he put in a CD that he'd probably brought from Minsk. "Ay-da, da, ay-da! Ay-da, da, ay-da! Ey oonayem! Ey ti Volga…" My mother didn't seem to notice; she was looking out the window silently. Afraid she would start yelling or try to get out of the car, I decided to remain quiet.

It took two hours to get from Sheepshead Bay to Riverdale in the midday traffic. My mind wandered to the time this little old lady sitting next to me in the back of the car was a young woman with wavy hair and beautiful dark eyes. I remembered the hateful look in her eyes when she slapped me across the face or screamed at me for buying the wrong bread or losing the change on the way home. Lost in reflection for most of the trip, when we turned into the park-like lawn next to the Hudson, I turned to my mother and said, "Isn't this beautiful, Mom?"

To my utter surprise, she smiled. "Oh, I didn't even realize you were there. Who are you?" Relief. She had completely forgotten about Harbor House and Galena.

As we turned into the entrance of the Hebrew Home, the security guard raised the gate and Vladimir drove us up the hill to the entry area. Two boys ran on the lawn while their mother chatted with their grandfather at one of the picnic tables overlooking the river. Vladimir unpacked the bags as I helped my mother out of the car and into the lobby.

"This is a beautiful place," my mother exclaimed, as I called the nursing station on the "moderate dementia" floor to announce our arrival. She seemed fascinated by the array of "First Ladies of the United States" behind a glass display window and she began to read the names of them out loud to no one in particular: "Martha Washington, Abigail Adams..." She smiled, seeming pleased with herself. "Dolly Madison, Rachel Jackson...."

Finally, a young African American man wearing a white lab coat over jeans and a T-shirt approached us and asked my mother if she was Molly. I thought about how much aggravation that name had caused me. I had spent six months doing the paper work necessary for my mother's eligibility for Medicaid. I had to get a copy of her social security card, her birth certificate, back bank statements and three years of cancelled checks.

All my life my mother told me that her real name was "Martha," but her nickname was "Molly." Her friends and family called her Molly, but her boss and colleagues at work always called her Martha. I assumed that was her legal name—her social security card and marriage certificate said "Martha." But when I finally got her birth certificate, the name on it was "Molly." She was also one year older than I had thought.

The young aide brushed aside his dreadlocks, put the bags on a rolling cart, and asked us to follow him. Soon we arrived at the second floor which was to be my mother's new home. Dolores, the Filipino head nurse, greeted us warmly and introduced us to the other nurses, as well as to the doctor who would give my mother an intake examination. The nurses gushed in their various Caribbean accents about how nice my mother was and she was smiling broadly. The doctor, an attractive Indian woman in her thirties, came over to introduce herself.

"Hello, I am Dr. Gupta and I will be examining you as soon as you settle in your room."

A thin elderly woman in chinos and an Adidas tennis shirt stood next to the doctor. I wondered who she was. Then Dolores introduced the woman to my mother.

"Martha, this is Emily. Emily, this is Martha." My mother smiled at Emily, but she scowled in return. As we walked down the hall to see my mother's new room, we passed a public bathroom with the door open. One of the aides was washing the linoleum floor and we could smell the Clorox and a whiff of urine. Emily began to curse. "Where the fuck do you think she's going? She's not going to my room. If she thinks she's going to be in my room, she's got another thing coming. This is my room and no one is taking it from me!"

Fearing that Emily might get violent toward my mother, I turned to Dolores and said, "My mother can't stay in this room. Is there another?"

"Yes, there's another one down the hall that's very nice."

"Good, let's look at that one. Has the woman in that room had it to herself for several months? Is she likely to have a tantrum as well?"

"No, I think it will be okay." Dolores assured me, patting my arm. "I'll show you the room."

I looked at my mother to see how she was responding to the commotion. She looked peaceful and unaffected. When she caught me looking at her, she said, "Aren't the people here nice?"

Mary Elizabeth

Mary Elizabeth had quit her job several months earlier to take pre-med classes required to apply to medical school. But she had finished the classes in early January, and it was now March, but she had neither gotten a job nor applied to medical school. In the last session I had asked her about it, and she had gotten angry at me. She had been careful over the years to keep her anger in check and not to let any of it out on me. So I thought it was an important breakthrough.

"Hi Mary Elizabeth," I greeted her. She was reading one of the magazines in the waiting room and looked up at me with a reassuring smile as if to say, "Don't worry, that was yesterday. I'm not angry anymore."

"I was reading about the crazy reaction to Ed Muskie crying. He's probably going to lose the nomination because of it. I'd like to see Nixon crying!" she said.

I nodded.

"I had a dream," she said, "that took place in my apartment but it looked like your waiting room. This man murdered my sister and was coming after me. I locked myself in, bolted the doors and windows. He acted like it was a bust. I was in my room and a friend said to open the window. The man got in with a gun and I was terrified. Someone in the dream was someone I knew. She was in cahoots with him—giving him instructions how to get in. I was so upset. I was furious."

"What comes to mind about a man murdering your sister and coming after you?"

"My father." She wailed.

"So you locked yourself up?"

"Yes... I think I locked it up inside me for all these years."

"What comes to mind about 'a bust'?"

"He was looking for something illegal or illicit."

"And your friend said to open the window?"

"Yes, I think that's you telling me to let my feelings come in to the room. To stop being locked up inside." She crossed her ankles.

"And what about the man with the gun getting in?"

"I think that's my father..."

"Yes, but I wonder if those are also your own murderous impulses. I wonder if the woman who's in cohoots with him is me."

"Because you want me to open the window to my rage."

"Yes, exactly."

Mary Elizabeth put her arms across her chest as if she was hugging herself and I saw she was weeping. "I'm furious at you."

I remembered how angry I used to get at Joan—for having a dog, for having a daughter, for having a life that didn't include me.

"Can you tell me about it?" I asked gently.

"I don't want to ... I was at Union Square Park before I came here, and I started thinking that I want to have a session there. I want us to get coffee and sit on the grass and have a session...."

She was quiet for a few moments.

"Can you tell me more about having a session in the park?"

"I don't want our relationship to just be here in this room. I want to take a walk with you, go out for coffee ..."

"Be friends?"

She bolted up from the couch and turned to me.

"Yes, exactly. I don't want to be your patient. I want us to be friends."

I was intimately acquainted with this feeling—I'd wanted the same thing with Joan. But I had learned that friendship and analysis were different solar systems. Both Mary Elizabeth and I experienced the analyst as the sun and felt like one of the many planets who revolve around her. But the reality is and was that in analysis the patient's experience is at the center of the universe and the analyst works to understand the world from the patient's viewpoint.

I had learned, since my analysis ended, that that is indeed the only relationship, in adult life at least, in which the other person under-stands your experience so completely because the analyst is trained to separate out her own experience. Of course, she never succeeds, it re-mains a goal, but a good analyst gets pretty close. The analytic rela-tionship takes a long time to mature and it's distilled and intense. But now that Joan was no longer my analyst, my experience was no longer at the center of our shared universe, not just because she was dying, but because I was no longer her patient.

"I think you experience me as keeping you at arm's distance. Or maybe, more accurately, 'oar's distance.' But I think our relationship, the analytic relationship, is completely different and in many ways more intimate than friendship. You have many close friends—you don't need another friend. You need me as your analyst."

"But it's not the same with my friends," she shook her head.

"No, that's the point," I said, leaning forward in my chair. "If I were your friend it wouldn't be the same either. It wouldn't be the same rela-tionship taking place in the park. It would be a different relationship."

"I'm not convinced," she said, making fists with her hands.

I smiled in recognition.

"We're going to have to stop for now."

>>><<<

When Mary Elizabeth left, I listened to my phone messages. My cousin Allan had left a message. Allan was my Aunt Hannah's son, more than fifteen years my senior, but we've had a special bond that goes back to when I was in elementary school and he was in the army. I wrote letters to him and he always wrote me back. One time when I was ten years old, he was in the army stationed at Fort Dix in New Jersey and came to Brooklyn to visit us.

"Hi, Rose," Allan had laughed as he picked me up and suspended me in air.

"Hi, Allan." I cried and giggled breathlessly.

He had put me down carefully and said, "So what have you been thinking about lately?"

"I've been thinking about segregation—do you know that it's legal in the South? It's amazing—the Supreme Court ruled unanimously that segregation in public schools is unconstitutional! Maybe that will change things...."

Allan laughed.

"Really!" I had insisted. "Black people can't even vote in the South!" I looked up at him.

"I know," he said. "I know."

After the army Allan had moved to London because he got a job teaching the children of military personnel in a school outside of London. It was there that he met and married Margaret and had two children. For years, I had brimmed over with excitement when I saw the blue airmail envelope addressed to me. Now he was visiting New York and wanted to see me.

"Let's have lunch, catch up and visit your mother," he suggested on the phone. "But I'm sure the food there is awful at the nursing home, so maybe you can find someplace in the neighborhood."

My mother got disoriented when I took her out of the nursing home so I didn't suggest including my mother in our lunch plans.

"There's a Jewish deli right around the corner from the nursing home," I said, "so we can have a corned beef sandwich and then go see Mom."

"Perfect." Allan seemed delighted that, like Houdini, I had transformed a potentially perilous experience (eating at the Hebrew Home) into an adventure.

Being with Joan

It had been four months since I began visiting Joan. At the beginning I visited her every other week, but as she got increasingly weaker and needed help twenty-four hours a day, I came more often. She didn't want a nurse; she wanted to be cared for by people who loved her. A hospice nurse visited every day, but Rachel organized people in shifts to stay with Joan. There was a constant flow of psychoanalysts bringing bagels, pizza, corned beef and pastrami. When Rachel asked me if I would like to take one of the shifts, I felt invited to join an elite group. After a couple of months of day shifts, I asked Rachel if she would like me to cover one of the nights. Rachel was exhausted—her shoulders were slumped and she was losing weight. Although she was tall and beautiful, when you looked in her big brown eyes she was a just a child about to be orphaned.

She had chosen to go to Barnard over Penn and Smith so that she could be close to her mother. She was shuttling back and forth between school and home, trying to oversee her mother's care. Although she was clearly grateful, when I volunteered for a night shift, she said she would have to ask Joan how she felt about my staying at night. Of course I understood the need to consult Joan, but I feared she might not be comfortable with such intimacy. The next time I came, Rachel told me Joan was touched that I was willing to do night duty. I could barely contain my gratitude.

When I arrived for my first night shift, Maria was leaving and told me Joan had bed sores on her back and I'd have to put cream on them after she took a shower. I assured her I would take good care of her. The next morning I made very strong coffee just the way I had learned she liked it and went into her bedroom to announce that breakfast was ready. She was awake and had already put her wig on. She smiled when I entered the room; her eyes took me in appreciatively. Her voice was barely audible. "Thank you," she said. I pulled off the blanket and she grimaced in pain as I propped her up off the pillow, helping her to first sit up and then move her legs off the bed.

"I'm sorry it hurts," I murmured as I hugged her tenderly.

She struggled to stand up, holding on to the walker. "I know. It's all right. I can do it."

I was hoping she'd be able to eat that morning. Now that I knew what she liked, I went out of my way to please her. I brought smoked salmon from Zabar's and bagels from H&H. We sat at her kitchen table having breakfast for a long time.

Buster had been lying quietly near the table, but he got up and came over to Joan and barked. She gave him a piece of her bagel.

"I'll take Buster for a walk before you take a shower, okay?"

"Really?" Joan said with a laugh. "Remember how upset you used to get about my dog?"

"Yes, I was furious at you for having a dog when you knew I didn't like dogs. How's that for feeling like I should be the center of the universe?"

"Well, it's just like your mother, right? She was always yelling at you for not knowing what she wanted without her telling you."

"It's not just that. It's that she was angry at me for not living my life according to what she wanted in her life."

310

"You mean you wanted me not to have a dog because you didn't like dogs."

"Yes, exactly." I smiled at her and kissed the top of her wig as I went to get the leash and attach it to Buster's collar. In the weeks that I'd been caring for Joan, I'd grown to like Buster. He often came and sat next to my chair and put his head on my lap as if he was asking me to scratch his back. I liked the sounds of contentment he made when I massaged him just behind his head.

When I returned to the apartment with Buster, I helped Joan from her chair to her walker. We slowly walked into her bedroom to prepare her to take a shower. She sat on the bed and took off her wig. Her skull was completely smooth, not a hair on her head. I kissed her naked scalp and bent down to take off the special socks that were supposed to keep her ankles from swelling. But her ankles were already the width of her thighs. They were red and blotchy. Then I helped her take off her nightgown. She used the walker to get to the shower door, then she handed it to me. I asked her to wait a minute so I could turn on the warm water before she stepped into the shower and sat on the cold metal seat. Once I warmed the seat, I helped her into the shower and held her arm until she sat firmly on the chair. She sighed from the exertion and then moaned with pleasure as the warm water spilled over shoulders.

I had been apprehensive about helping her shower. I was afraid of being awkward and I didn't know how I would feel seeing her body. For years it had been taboo to know anything about Joan's life and now I was going to see her completely exposed. In recent years, I tried to avoid seeing my mother naked. Whenever I had to see her body, I was nauseated by the way her dried out breasts hung on her. I hated to look at her belly protruding over the almost white pubic hair that covered her cleft. It was the same feeling I have when I look at someone who's missing a limb, I want to turn away. Maybe it's because I don't want to know that could happen to me. My belly protrudes too. It runs in the family; all the women on my mother's side had bellies.

Her chest was flat and she had no nipples; I stood outside the shower to make sure she did not fall.

When she stepped out I handed her a pink towel and helped her dry her back and feet. I could see the bedsores on her buttocks and I took a swab and dipped it in cream and dabbed the pink glop to cover the whole sore on each side. I was surprised that the physical intimacy didn't bother me. I wondered why.

My mother never bathed me or paid any attention to my body; she acted like it was invisible. When we went swimming during the summer at Sunset Pool or Brighton Beach, she never put up a towel to give me privacy while I was changing.

"Mom hold up the towel. I don't want everyone to see me."

"Don't be silly, no one can see anything. Just put on your bathing suit."

"Mommy, everyone else's mother holds up a towel," I pleaded.

"I don't care what everyone else does. Just put on your bathing suit."

My mother never put her arm around me when we stood next to each other or spontaneously brushed the hair from my face with her hand. She didn't even hold my hand when we walked down the street.

Joan sighed with relief from the coolness of the cream on the open wounds. Dying took away any reticence she might have had. Or maybe I had mistaken her behaving like a psychoanalyst for reticence. After she settled onto the bed, I crouched below her and rubbed lotion on her swollen ankles and feet. She moaned from the pleasure of being touched. I knew she had been divorced since Rachel was a little girl. I wondered now how long it had been since she had had hands on her that embraced and soothed her. My fingers moved up her leg, massaging the cream into her lonely skin. She sighed with pleasure—the way a baby coos when her mother picks her up and holds her close.

Then Joan put her hand on my shoulder and said, "Thank you. You take such good care of me." She wasn't bitter about dying, just grateful to be taken care of in a loving way.

I bit my lip. "I want to be as close to you as I can before I lose you."

For the first time, tears rolled down her face. "That's how I feel. I want to be as close to the people I love as I can before I have to leave them. That's why I don't want any nurses. I want people who love me to take care of me."

I didn't feel the same way. I wouldn't want Stephen or my friends to take care of me when I was dying. Afraid they would be repulsed or burdened, I'd rather have a stranger, an Irish hospice nurse, who didn't know me when I had been full of life and able to take care of myself.

"Howiya? What's da starry? Are ya hurtin'?" she would say.

"No, I'm not in any pain now."

"Ah dah's grand, so it is!"

I took Joan's hand and put it on my mouth, kissing her palm. "I love you true and blue and like glue."

Her tears came down faster now, "I know."

I had waited so long for Joan to say she loves me. For so long I imagined she had pushed me away because I wanted too much intimacy. I didn't want to leave after 45 minutes. I wanted to be part of her life outside the consultation room. I assumed she wanted me to go away because I wanted too much. But that was my mother who wanted me to leave her alone—stay out on the porch. Joan was just being my analyst and setting limits to maximize the transference.

I had wanted to know how she felt and what she experienced. Did she have a man in her life? What was it like to be a divorced mother? Where did she go on vacation? How did she feel about me? She wouldn't tell me. I was her patient. Now I wanted to take care of her; to express my gratitude and my love for her. Finally, she was letting me.

Visiting Mom

The elevator door opened to the familiar smell of disinfectant. There was one aide in a white lab coat at the nurse's station and the halls were empty. Allan and I could hear some music at the end of the floor and assumed we would find my mother there. Passing by a string of empty rooms, each with two metal beds and small dressers, we noticed that next to each door there was a sign with the names of the two occupants and their pictures.

Allan took off his glasses and moved closer to look at the pictures and said, "I wonder if they do this so the aides know who is in each room?" He tilted his bald head slightly to the right and looked quizzical. It was a warm Saturday in May and he was wearing a short-sleeved shirt and shorts.

I hypothesized, "Maybe it's for the occupants. Do you think that some of them don't know their names anymore and need pictures?"

"Well," he said thoughtfully, "if they don't know their names, they probably wouldn't recognize their pictures either."

"Good point, my dear Watson."

At the end of the corridor my mother was sitting with a group of ten or twelve women who were singing and dancing to 1940s and '50s songs played by a slim, gray-haired man with a hearing aid. We greeted her and she looked at us quizzically as if to say, "I know I know you, but I don't know who you are." I was used to it by then, but Allan turned to me and whispered, "She has no idea who we are." I smiled in agreement. I wasn't sad that my mother didn't know who I was. After all, what would she say if she knew? "Where have you been?" "Why didn't you come earlier?" "Why haven't you called?" "Why are you leaving me here?" Yes, it was okay with me that she didn't know who I was; she was kinder to strangers.

The volunteer played songs on a keyboard that had so many lights and buttons that it looked like a cockpit. I thought to myself that he was about 70 years old, but he must feel young and spry being surrounded by a dozen women between 90- and 100-years-old with dementia. My mother was the only one close to his age. He wasn't talking to any of the women, just fiddling with the controls on the bizarre instrument. Clearly, he didn't feel identified with them. While they were wearing outfits from their previous lives with stains from meals gone by, he was dressed in well-pressed light green chino shorts and a dark green polo with a Ralph Lauren pony label over his heart. Having trouble with the keyboard, he leaned over, touched my arm with his deeply veined hand, and whispered, "I just bought it and I'm not used to it yet." I nodded and smiled, to be supportive.

Then he started to sing and play. "I'm gonna sit right down and write myself a letter...." My mother and several others sang along, but off tune, and two or three beats late. "I'm gonna sit right down ..."

He finished that one and started to belt out: "When the moon hits your eye like a big pizza pie, that's amore...." I closed my eyes for a second and saw my mother ironing in the kitchen while she was listening to the wooden radio on the table next to the ironing board. She was singing along with Dean Martin as wafts of steam jumped up from my father's white shirt.

Now, my mother waited a few seconds and after Dorothy chanted, "That's amore...," she sang with her shakey voice, "That's amore...."

The frail Black woman smiled supportively at my mother. She was missing one of her front teeth, but it was hardly noticeable because her white hair and sparkling eyes drew attention away from her mouth.

Then he played Perry Como tunes. The heavy woman with the portable oxygen began immediately, "A, you're adorable ... B, you're so beautiful." Then the others joined in: "C, you're a cutie full of charms." My mother couldn't remember the words exactly, but she hummed the tune and beckoned Allan and me to join in: "D, you're a darling and E, you're exciting...."

By the time he began playing, "I love you a bushel an' a peck," the anorexic-looking woman who had been sleeping while standing in her walker woke up and joined in without missing a beat: "A bushel and a peck and a hug around the neck...."

Allan and I smiled at each other, as if to say, "I guess she's all right." We both gave her a kiss and walked toward the elevator. We could hear the gray-haired man singing behind us, "Our love affair was too hot not to cool down." A few seconds later, just as we stepped on to the open elevator, we heard several off-tune creaky voices: "Too hot..."

Sally: The Last Session

Since we started to talk about Sally's conflict about what kind of a "mother" she wanted me to be, things had gotten much warmer between us and I no longer dreaded opening the door of my office to greet her. She still criticized me from time to time, but both of us understood it as her attempt to push me away. When I opened the door Sally was wearing a pair of jeans and a sleeveless blouse. I could see the shallow wrinkles on her cheeks that flowed through deep crevices next to her eyes and finally came to rest in dark lakes under her eyes. She came to her appointment unadorned.

"I feel I'm opening up in some way," she said, "but I'm afraid that what has been underneath my tightness and control is a bottomless depression. It's so intense. I can hardly bear it."

Part of me was frightened for her. I wondered what would happen if she got in touch with the deep-rooted pain that had been locked away for years and had never seen the light of day. For some reason I thought about the prescribed burns they do in national forests. When you see the black stumps and broken trees it's hard to imagine conservationists having done it on purpose. How could all that destruction be healthy for the forest? But, ironically, prescribed burning recycles nutrients and increases plant growth.

"I know you are in a lot of pain and it feels bottomless, but it isn't. I think you need to first experience how vulnerable you feel so that we can start a new growth process."

"I never wanted a woman analyst," Sally was crying so hard it was difficult for her to speak at the same time, "because I didn't want to feel this..."

"But you came to me and you've stuck it out. So part of you wanted to deal with these feelings."

She remembered a dream. She said she was going to be in a play and told Jessica about it and when she looked at her face, she thought she was disappointed in her. She imagined Jessica thinking, "Wow, this person was really hurt early." But then Jessica gestured to Sally as if to say: "Come here, I'll help you. I have something good for you."

"What made you remember the dream just then?" I asked, wondering if this was a positive transference dream. The muscles in my back relaxed.

"You were reassuring me before and I think that's what reminded me. I woke up with the feeling that she cared about me."

"When did you have the dream?" I asked.

"After our last session."

"So it sounds like Jessica is a stand in for me."

"Sure. She referred me." She whimpered. "I feel you want me to get the most out of treatment and out of my life.... It gives me a headache to think about it. I never felt my mother cared about me. She was so involved with how things looked to other people, but she never cared about my feelings. My head is pounding."

She fumbled in her purse trying to find aspirin, but she didn't have any.

"I know we have time left," she said, "but I can't sit here without taking something for my headache. I'm going to leave and go to the drugstore."

"Okay, if the pain is that bad we can stop for now." Part of me wanted to make an interpretation about what was giving her a headache, but I thought better of it.

She picked up her purse, solemnly said goodbye, and left the office.

⤛⤜

I wasn't upset when Sally left; I assumed it was a psychosomatic symptom. I used the remaining time to make some calls before my next patient arrived.

Several hours later, my office phone rang in the house.

"Hello, you don't know me. My name is Mary Beth Emerson. I'm calling with some bad news—Sally Atkins died today."

"Oh no," I gasped. "How could that be? I just saw her."

"I know," her voice sounded empathic and calm. "It was very sudden." She must be a therapist, I thought. Many of Sally's friends were therapists.

"What happened?" My eyes bulged.

"It seems that she left your office and called Jonathan to say she had a really bad headache and he should pick up food for dinner. Then she went to the subway and collapsed on the platform. Some bystander called 911 but she was dead when the EMS guys got there. They think it was an aneurism."

All the air had been sucked out of the room and I couldn't breathe. How could I have let her walk out of the room when she complained of a headache? The guilt enveloped me—a blanket that I was struggling to get out from under. She had told me many times that something was

321

wrong with her brain and I assumed it was a metaphor or an anxiety attack that was related to all her past traumas.

I imagined the scene at the subway. She must have barely made it down the long corridor to the N train and then held the railing tightly on the staircase as people pushed on all sides to get to the train before the doors closed. When she got to the platform, feeling wobbly and disoriented, the pain in her head must have been excruciating and her knees gave out. She fell on the platform and people, unsure of whether she was sick or a drunk, initially approached her apprehensively until they realized she was having a stroke or heart attack. Then a young woman screamed, "She's dying. Help her. Someone help her." But by the time help came it was too late.

"The funeral will be Friday at 10 a.m. if you'd like to come," Mary Beth went on.

I managed to say, "Yes, thank you for calling...." Our work had just gotten off the ground and she was dead.

My Mother Is Dying

Asleep in her wheelchair with her head slumped on her chest, my mother looked dead when I arrived. Her left foot was bandaged and she wasn't wearing a shoe. When I asked Lulu, the smiling Jamaican aide with a lilt in her voice, what was going on, she said my mother had an infection in her bunion and the bandage couldn't fit in her shoe. Her toes were misshapen and piled on top of each other like a teetering stack of wood. Looking closely, I realized she was wearing an ankle-high stocking over the bandage that was so tight the blood was not circulating to her foot. The tight elastic had created a deep groove just above her ankle. Beneath the groove, her ankle had a purplish hue and was swollen to twice its normal size. A wave of nausea rose up and I started to retch. My mother couldn't protest or ask for relief. She was helpless. I didn't even know if she felt pain or discomfort. I frantically removed the stocking and started rubbing her leg with both hands trying to get the circulation back.

I had not been to see her for two weeks because Stephen and I had been in France in late July to celebrate our second anniversary. I chided myself for being just like my mother—so negligent and oblivious I hadn't noticed a worsening infection. After all, Sally had told me there was something wrong with her brain and I hadn't done anything to help her. I just listened to her. I could feel the tension in my chest getting tighter and tighter.

"What's wrong with you," I yelled at Lulu, "she could end up with gangrene and need to have her foot amputated."

Suddenly Lulu's usually understandable accent turned to patois. "Mi would rada you talk to mi."

"I'm talking to you because you put this stocking on her foot and didn't pay attention to how tight it was."

"Why yu fe galang so?"

I wasn't sure what that meant, but I was furious and wanted someone to take responsibility. It was time for my mother to die, but I couldn't stand the idea of someone killing her. I ran down the hall to find Dolores. When I found her, I was frantic and out of breath.

"What's the matter?" She looked startled.

I struggled not to raise my voice, but my voice was cracking, "One of the aides dressed my mother this morning and put a stocking on her swollen leg that is so tight it stopped the circulation. Her foot is blue for Christ sake."

"Okay, take it easy, I'll tell Lulu not to put those stockings on your mother anymore. Don't worry." She put her hand on my shoulder reassuringly.

I wasn't sure I could trust her. What if tomorrow was her day off? What if someone else replaced Lulu? My tears erupted again. I couldn't let them do that to my mother. I went to her room and looked for the knee highs in her drawer. When I was sure I had found all of them, I threw them in the trash in the hall to make sure no one thoughtlessly used them again. Then I headed back to see my mother.

She was still sleeping soundly, her head awkwardly tilted forward. I wondered if she could feel a kink in her neck. Checking her ankle, I was relieved to see the indentation seemed to be going away. I went to her room to get some moisturizing cream for her. The dried pink hydrangeas I had put on her bureau had turned brown and were falling apart. I picked up the cream and ran down the hall to my mother. I massaged her calf and ankle between my hands for another few minutes to make sure the circulation was coming back. Her parched skin, stretched from swelling, soaked up the cream. She was still sleeping when I headed for the elevator. I was relieved, but guilty. What if I hadn't visited today? What if this had gone on another week?

Joan Coming to the End

Rachel opened the door when I rang the bell and told me Joan was in bed.

"How is she?" I asked.

She wasn't wearing any makeup and her eyes were filled with sadness. She rubbed her face. "Not good. She was up vomiting during the night, but she's sleeping now." Rachel was exhausted. It had been months since the round-the-clock vigil had started and she had borne the brunt of it.

Standing on my tip toes, I put my arms around her tall, lanky frame. Brushing her long brown hair from her wet cheeks, I held her tight. Rachel did not look like Joan; she had a completely different body type—maybe like her father. I had no idea. But her mannerisms mirrored Joan's. She had Joan's dimples and when she smiled she tilted her head a bit to the right when she said something emotional like Joan did. And although her eyes were brown and Joan's were blue, they had the same warm twinkle.

When I stopped hugging her, I said, "Why don't you get some sleep now, I can stay until five."

"Yes, that would be good. The hospice nurse is coming later. I'll take Buster out for a walk now—it's such a beautiful fall day, and then I'll go back to the dorm and take a nap." She walked over to the table and picked up the leash and called Buster. The two of them left and I went into Joan's room to see if she was still sleeping.

Joan was lying on her back, snoring. Her bald head was turned to the side and I could see how puffy her face had become from steroids. She had dark half-moons under her eyes. I sat in a chair next to her bed and put my hand on hers—being careful not to pull out the intravenous fluid tube in her arm. Tracing the veins in her hand with my finger, I listened to her inhale, sometimes a snore, sometimes an almost silent breath, and waited expectantly for her to exhale. I watched her chest go up as her lungs took in each mouthful of air, and down as she let it out. The skin around her neck had brown spots from the summers on the beach when Rachel was a little girl. All those Augusts that I suffered through, counting the days until Joan would come back to me. This time she was not going to come back.

Mary Elizabeth

When I opened the door to the waiting room, Mary Elizabeth was reading the *Times* while holding a bouquet of yellow and orange roses. "The government of the Republic of Ireland has finally removed the special position of the Catholic Church from the Irish Constitution! Remember this date, January 5, 1973," she said gleefully.

She walked into the office and announced with a big smile, "I want to hug you," and she did. Surprised at how perfectly comfortable I felt, I thanked her for the flowers.

"Let me put these in some water," I said, "and then we can talk about to what I owe this happy surprise." I put the flowers in a vase and sat down.

Mary Elizabeth didn't lie down. She sat up and seemed to be admiring the flowers.

"So?" I said.

"Well, first of all, I'm smiling inside because of the Catholic Church finally getting thrown out of the Irish Constitution!"

I smiled. "Is there anything else?"

"Yes, I felt powerful after last session," she said. "I just felt empowered by it."

"What was it exactly?"

"It gave me confidence, you really got it. You hit the nail on the head, when you said my refusal to get a job was a tantrum and that I was in a rage. I wasn't in touch with it when you said it, but then it all came together—repeating my relationship with my mother with you, being angry at you, refusing to come or to get a job."

"So it gave you confidence in me?" I asked.

"Well, yes, but in me too, because I was the one who connected what I'm doing now to what I did when I came back from Africa. It made me feel I'm understanding myself better; I'm moving in the right direction. We're on top of what's going on with me. It made me feel like, 'Okay, I can do this; I can get a job and handle this.'"

"So it sounds like it made you feel confident in 'us.'"

"I was angry at you because we've focused on the ways I keep people away—all the walls and layers of protection. Now they're almost all down and I feel you are the one behind a wall. You are the one who keeps everything that really matters to you hidden from me. You won't let me know you or be close to you. I think that's what I'm so angry about."

"I wonder how what you're talking about is related to your coming in and hugging me."

"You mean it was getting past that wall I imagine you have?" She smiled.

"Yes, I think so."

She remembered a dream. She was talking to one of her professors and she said, "What's the name of the book you gave me about the link between Africa and rice cultivation in South Carolina?" It had a girl-friend quality. Mary Elizabeth felt a special connection to her—they had a history. She felt the professor needed something from her. But she didn't remember the name of the book. She promised to get the name of the book, but she left her purse in the professor's office. The professor put it outside her office for Mary Elizabeth to pick up because she was having a meeting with another student.

I realized it was a transference dream and I was the professor. "What was the feeling in the dream?" I asked.

"I was briefly inside her special orbit but it wasn't permanent; I was pushed out."

"What do you think made you think of the dream just then?" I asked.

"I want to be in your inner circle—a girlfriend. The professor is you," she said.

"But I pushed you out?"

"Yes, but I was going to go away and do my own research; I had my own resources. I wasn't alone without any means of my own. I just remembered my friend Peggy moved the day I had the dream."

"It sounds like leaving is on your mind," I said.

"Yes. I just realized I forgot to bring your check." She slapped the couch.

"What do you make of that?" I asked, half smiling.

"Well, not bringing the check is about not wanting to have to pay you. I want to be your friend.

"In the dream I put the purse outside the door.

"All my stuff is in my purse and my money is in there," she said. "You put it outside for me to pick up. You're giving me my money and my self to come and pick up. The purse is like myself."

"It sounds like you're ambivalent," I said. "Part of you doesn't want to leave treatment; you want to continue as friends. But another part of you feels ready to go—you have your own resources now that you have a job. You're earning a living; you can take your money and yourself with you..."

"Yes, I see that. But I'm not ready yet!" She nodded.

"We're going to have to stop for now."

⫸⫷

Mary Elizabeth got up from the couch, picked up her things, and turned to look at me. She smiled and threw me a kiss as she left. We both knew she was coming to the end of her treatment.

My Mother Dies

I was in the middle of a session with Dave, but saw the answering machine light up to indicate there was a call. I didn't answer it. But I had an eerie feeling that my mother was dead. Dave was staring at the floor, so he didn't see me looking at the phone. He was talking about graduate school.

"I'm not going to turn in the dissertation proposal on the due date," he said.

"Why is that?" I asked.

"They just make up the due date to suit their convenience," he said, shaking his head from side to side. "I'm not going to suit their needs."

My mind wandered from Dave to a conversation I had had a week earlier with Dr. Gupta. She had called to say the infection in my mother's bunion had gotten much worse.

"Do you want her to be sent to the hospital?" she asked.

"If this was your mother would you send her to the hospital?" I asked, biting the inside of my cheek.

"No...," she said hesitantly, "if it was my mother I wouldn't do it. She doesn't get out of bed; she just sleeps. She doesn't eat; we're trying to feed her, but she won't take anything. I think it's time."

"I can't tell you how much it means to me to get an honest answer from a doctor. Thank you. I have to think about it."

I called Stephen.

"Dr. Gupta called and said the infection is very bad," I told him, "and I have to decide whether to send her to the hospital for intravenous antibiotics."

"Well," he asked, "what will happen if you don't?"

"She'll die." I bit my lip.

"Oh," he sounded shocked. "Well, she's going to die very soon. If you send her to the hospital she will be fed intravenously and lie there like a vegetable. She won't get better, she just won't die yet."

"I don't want to feel that I like I'm killing her. After all I've spent so many years wanting to kill her that the idea of *really* killing her is scary."

"If it were my mother," he said gently, "I wouldn't send her to the hospital. I wouldn't prolong it. But I want you to feel okay about yourself."

I breathed a sigh of relief into the phone. That's what I needed—a way of letting her die that would not make me feel that I killed her.

"When you're angry," Stephen said, "it's hard to let your mother die…" I called Dr. Gupta after I hung up the phone with Stephen and told her not to send my mother to the hospital.

Now, I turned my attention back to Dave.

"What do you imagine will happen if you don't hand in your dissertation proposal on time?" I asked slowly.

"They might throw me out of the program," he said nonchalantly.

I wanted to yell at him, "Are you crazy? Why are you acting out the same dynamic with your mother all over again? You'll get thrown out of graduate school." But I took a deep breath and calmed myself.

"Dave, how will you feel if you get thrown out of graduate school?" I asked.

"I'll be fine," he scoffed, "I'm not going to cave in to some stupid deadline." I could see the hair on his chest peeking out of his mis-buttoned shirt.

"Dave, you're being quite self-destructive here. It's like refusing to eat because you don't want to give your mother any satisfaction," I said.

"I know ... but I don't care. I'm not going to cave in," he said, shaking his head.

"Do you think this might be related to your not paying your last two bills from me?" I dug my nails into the palms of my hands.

Dave looked down at the floor and then crossed his arms and looked at me.

"Yeah, I don't feel like paying you. You just do this to make money and I don't want to give you my money." He nodded as if he was agreeing with himself.

"Well, it's true that this is the way I make a living, so I have to charge patients for working with them," I said. I sat on my hands.

He was quiet. He looked at the ceiling and then at the books in my bookcases.

"Does it feel like I'm doing this for my own good," I asked, "and I'm not really interested in you?" I raised one brow.

He continued looking at the bookcases for a while. "Yes, this isn't for me, it's for you to make money," he said, not looking at me. He crossed his arms over his chest.

"Dave, these are not mutually exclusive categories. Just because I make a living at this doesn't mean that I'm not interested in helping you. After all, you want to be a psychologist yourself. Are you only doing it for the money?"

He rubbed the back of his neck. "No ...," he said.

"Look," I leaned forward in my chair, "this is all about your relationship with your mother. You felt everything she did was for her and to your detriment. But it's possible for both people in a relationship to get something out of it. It's not a zero-sum game."

He looked at the door and then the floor. "I won't be doing therapy because of the money. I will be doing it to help people … but that's not true of most people who do therapy. Most of them just want to make money."

"Dave," I said with as much restraint as I could muster, "you are paying me six dollars per session. Do you know that is a greatly reduced fee?" I dug my nails into my palms again.

"Yes," he said looking at the floor.

"So, how can you insist I'm working with you because of the money?"

He was quiet.

"Well, we are going to have to stop for now," I said after a few minutes.

As soon as Dave's session ended, I finally listened to the message. It was Dr. Gupta. "I'm sorry to have to tell you that your mother passed away this morning. Please call me to let me know if you want to see her before they take her out of her room."

I sighed. When I was in treatment with Joan I used to tell her that I couldn't stop seeing her until my mother died because I expected to be torn apart by it. She had disagreed. "I don't think you have to be so frightened. I think you've been dealing with separating from your mother for a long time and when the ultimate separation happens, I think you'll be sad, but fine." I imagined my head leaning on her shoulder and my tears falling on her apple-green sweater.

I thought about my mother's body. It had never been a place of refuge for me. She had never invited me to seek comfort in her arms any more than in her words. I didn't want to hold on to her. Indeed, I'd spent most of my life trying to get away from her—going to college in California and hating myself every time I said or did anything that reminded me of her. I called Stephen.

"She's dead," I said, whimpering. "They want to know if I want to see her body before they take her to the funeral home...." I bit the side of my mouth and wiped my cheek with my hand.

"Do you?" he asked incredulously.

"No... but do you think that's terrible of me?" I bawled.

"What? Are you crazy? I'd think you were crazy if you wanted to see her dead body!"

I laughed through my tears.

"Okay, I'll call Dolores and tell her, and I'll call the funeral home to finalize the arrangements."

Stephen and I had arranged the details with the funeral home weeks before. So all I had to do was tell them when the funeral would be.

The social worker at the nursing home told me they would pack my mother's clothing in cardboard boxes and leave them in the basement "Pick Up" office. I wasn't in a hurry to get them; we had moved my mother twice since my father died so there wasn't anything left that I valued. I thought about moving my mother from her apartment to the nursing home.

"Let's get the super to clean the apartment and let him take everything he wants," Stephen had said as he pushed the door to my parents' apartment.

"No, I can't do that," I said. My head was throbbing. "I have to sort through it. There's a lot of stuff here. A whole life."

"I can't stand it," he whispered. "You want me to go through all this crap with you?"

"No," I said, holding the back of my head. "I need to do this and it's clear that you can't help me. I'll call Linda."

"Linda hated your mother. Do you really want to call her to help you go through all this stuff?"

I imagined calling Linda. She didn't like my mother, but I knew she would come and help me.

"Stephen wants to throw everything out but the old pictures," I told her.

"He doesn't want anything and he just wants to get it over with. I know you didn't like my mother. But can you come and sift through all this with me?"

"Of course, I'll come. I don't know if I'll be much help, but I'll come."

"Yes, I just need you to sit with me as I do it. I just don't want to do it alone. Thanks."

Linda came an hour later. She kissed Stephen hello and he left. She gave me a long hug.

"Okay, let's do it," she said.

We sat on the floor in my parents' bedroom sorting through drawers with underwear and fifty-year-old love letters.

"Look at this!" Linda exclaimed.

She had found that old sex manual.

"I can't imagine your mother having sex!" she exclaimed.

"Me either," I agreed. I smiled, remembering all those torturous sessions with Joan on this very subject.

"Look at this," she said, turning to one of the pages that had been earmarked.

"Cunnilingus," she exclaimed. "Well good for Molly!"

The next day we sat on the floor in the living room and packed up the dishes my mother had so carefully placed in the breakfront. The "girl" dusted them every other week, but they were only used for Rosh Hashanah or dinner parties.

I used to feel contemptuous of everything in there, but I had found in recent years that I liked the elegance of silver ice tongs, Rosenthal tea cups and Lenox butter dishes. The fact that I wanted to use them, rather than display them, seemed to calm my anxiety about being like my mother.

When Linda and I turned to the closets, they were full of blouses and dresses with stains on them, yellowed from years without cleaning. Most of them were beyond resuscitation and we threw them in large black garbage bags. Some things would recover with dry cleaning, so we put them in a pile for the cleaner.

When we were finished, we dragged the bags and cartons we packed down to my car and packed it for the trip to Harbor House. When we unpacked it we realized much of it were things she would never wear again—for instance, silk blouses, wool knit suits, and a mink coat and stole. I guess I hadn't yet come to grips with the reality of what her life was going to be like at that point.

By the time I moved my mother from Harbor House to the nursing home, I knew what her life was going to be like. I had given the silk blouses, wool suits and mink stoles to Goodwill.

So now at the Hebrew Home I knew this was going to be a simple sorting operation—garbage or the Goodwill. Stephen came with me. It took us twenty minutes to find the "Pick Up" office. We guessed that the nursing home wasn't eager to advertise where all the residents were going to end up. When we finally got there, a skinny Black man with a bunch of keys hanging from his belt raised his head from *The New York Post* and grudgingly greeted us.

"Yes, what is the name of the deceased?" he asked coolly.

I didn't know if I should say Martha or Molly, I said, "eeny, meeny, miney, mo," and went with Molly.

"Molly Winer."

He looked up her name in a book with lined pages. "Okay, she's boxes 186, 187, and 188. Make a right out of the door and go into the first room on the right. You'll find them there. They're numbered."

Bingo, I thought. "Thank you."

Stephen looked upset. "Don't you think they should train them to say 'Sorry for your loss' or something?"

"That would be nice," I offered, "but you never know how people feel anyway."

I was touched that Stephen was feeling protective of me, but the truth was, I was eager to get this over with. I didn't want to linger. I didn't care what the man said. I just wanted to find those boxes and fill those garbage bags. We had brought large black bags and medium white ones; the black ones were garbage, and the white ones were for Goodwill. There was not much for Goodwill.

The funeral was at the grave site. Mount Ararat cemetery was a familiar place by then. My father, three uncles and aunts and two of my first cousins were buried there as was Stephen's father. I knew the ritual. The cars pulled up to the office and everyone got out, greeted one another, and ran to the bathroom. Then we all emerged from the rest rooms, chatted for a few minutes, got back in the cars, and drove to the grave site. After the service, we all kissed each other, got back in our cars, and inevitably got lost looking for the exit. From one death to another, we could not seem to remember the way out. But eventually, we all found our way back to Brooklyn for lox and bagels in someone's house.

This was going to be a small group with a totally different feeling. My mother's siblings were all dead and their children were spread far and wide; her friends had either died or moved to Florida. The only people coming were Rabbi Rothstein, my cousin Allan, his wife and two children, Stephen's mother, Linda, Stephen, and me.

340

When Rabbi Rothstein, who had not known my mother, asked if any of us wanted to say anything, there was a resounding silence.

Finally, Allan, feeling embarrassed by the silence, said he'd like to say something.

"My aunt Molly was a successful woman for her day." He shifted his weight from one foot to the other. I could see his breath in the cold December air. "She had a husband who loved her and a daughter who is very successful." He hesitated for a moment, fixing his wool scarf. "She and my uncle had a successful marriage, which was a model for all of us. After all, it's rare nowadays to have a family in which no one is divorced." Then he stopped, swabbed his eyes, and nodded at the rabbi to indicate that he was finished.

I had spent years thinking about what I would say when my mother died. I had spent sessions with Joan talking about it. I'd given eulogies for my Aunt Hannah and one of my friends who died of pancreatic cancer. And I'd spoken at my father's funeral. But now, on this cold December day, I could not think of anything appropriate to say about my mother. I had no funny anecdotes or touching memories to offer. I had come to my mother's funeral empty-headed.

The pressure was building. The rabbi waited. He appeared mildly annoyed—he fidgeted with his wool scarf with pursed lips and a quizzical look in his eyes. I imagined him thinking, "What's the matter with you people?" Finally, I had an epiphany and thought of something to say.

"My mother was not an easy person," I said. My shoulders relaxed. "She spent much of her life feeling deprived and angry. And most of that anger came out on me. But she had good reason. She was a very smart woman. If she had been born a generation later, she might have been an accountant or a business consultant instead of a bookkeeper and housewife. She had to depend on my father to make a living for the family and he was not as good a business person as she was. And although my father was crazy in love with her, she spent her life unsuccessfully trying to get her mother and her sister Gus to love and appreciate her. It was hard for her to nurture me, but I can think of a couple of instances in which, as a child, I was proud of her.

"When she was a young mother she had a close friend, Lillian, who died of tuberculosis. My mother and some of her friends organized the Lillian Sonnenshein League to raise money for tuberculosis hospitals. She and her friends had luncheons and auctions and gave the proceeds to hospitals in Lillian's name."

I could see Linda crying and the rabbi smiling. Stephen was teary and I heard Allan murmur, "I forgot about that."

"Another instance was with her friend Eleanor. My mother worked with her at a gas station on Coney Island Avenue. Eleanor was very depressed and I remember Mom used to talk to her on the phone and try to comfort her. Eventually she killed herself and Mom was beside herself with grief."

I heard Allan say, "I didn't know about that."

"So although Mom was a difficult and often unhappy woman, she was also capable of being loving and generous." I was proud of myself for not adding: "Just not to me." I turned to the rabbi and nodded to indicate I was finished.

The rabbi asked if anyone else wished to speak and when no one answered, he said we were ready to say Kaddish, the Jewish mourner's prayer. We all bowed our heads and joined her in the prayer:

Yis'ga'dal v'yis'kadash sh'may ra'bbo, b'olmo dee'vro chir'usay v'yamlich v'yisalal...

In concert we all said "Amen," and walked over to the grave site to see the grave diggers lower the maple coffin into the grave. They were both wearing chino uniforms with "Mount Ararat" embroidered on the left side of their chests. They put ropes under the casket and the tall, heavy set man picked up the ropes on the left side. His partner, a shorter man with a muscular build, picked up the ropes on the right side. Then slowly they lowered the coffin into the ground. The rabbi picked up the shovel and asked who wanted to shovel dirt into my mother's grave. I had been contained up to that point. But picking up a shovel and pouring dirt on my mother's casket opened a pocket of grief inside me that poured out uncontrollably. My head was throbbing. We were burying my mother, but all the years of love and hate, hope and disappointment, anger and regret would live on emblazoned inside me.

I thought about the day I would be inside the coffin and my daughter would be standing in Mount Ararat shoveling dirt on my casket. I wondered what she would feel. What would she say about her mother? Will she have trouble thinking of what to say about me at my funeral? Will she remember times we laughed until we cried? Will she feel she lost the person who loved her most in the world? Will she feel bereft? The thought of it made me convulse with spasms of anguish. I didn't feel those things about my mother and I was wailing at the horrific possibility that my daughter would not feel them when I died. I hoped she would have more to say about me, our relationship, and my life than I was able to conjure up about my mother.

⸎⸎⸎

When Stephen and I returned from the funeral, he got the mail. He handed me a hand-addressed envelope. I recognized the penmanship—it was from Dave. My eyes widened in anticipation of a past due check. But there was no check. Only a short note: "I won't be coming back to see you."

I covered my mouth and muttered, "Shit… that didn't work!" But then I took a deep breath and joined Stephen on the elevator.

Mary Elizabeth: the Last Session

For about a month before Mary Elizabeth's final session, every time I thought about it my stomach went into the rinse cycle. It was probably the cumulative loss and anticipation of further loss that made my stomach churn—my mother, Joan, Sally, Dave, and now Mary Elizabeth. But as the time got closer, I calmed down as if the machine had come to a stop.

When I opened the door to the waiting room, Mary Elizabeth was smiling and held a bouquet of red and white Asiatic lilies. The fragrance filled the waiting room and drifted into the office.

"These are for you," she said with a grin as she wiped her cheeks.

"Thank you. They're very beautiful." I wiped my eyes as I turned away to find a tall vase.

Mary Elizabeth went into my office and sat down on the couch while I searched for a tall vase and filled it with water. She had taken off her winter coat by the time I returned with the lilies in the vase and placed them on the coffee table. She admired them and said, "I think they're called Stargazers. That's an interesting name actually. Maybe it's because the flowers face up toward the sky. They're very beautiful aren't they?"

"Yes, they certainly are."

"I'd like to sit up for this session. Is that okay with you?"

She hadn't sat up in such a long time that it was strange to have her looking at me as she talked. She was going to see my tears which, I was sure, were going to be flowing at the end of the session. But, on the other hand, it would have felt odd to her to get up from lying on the couch and walk out the door forever.

"Sure, that's fine. But what do you feel about sitting up?"

"I guess I want to look at you for the last time," she said. "I want to take you in so I can hold onto you when I leave."

"I had a dream this morning," she said, "when I woke up."

"Yes?"

"I was in an optician's office and was being fitted for glasses. She tried on a few pairs, and then found a pair that looked really good. I said to the optician, 'I really like these.' The optician said, 'Good, but can you see clearly?' I answered, 'Yes, I can read the fine print.'"

"What was the feeling in the dream?" I asked.

"Confident. I liked the way I looked," she said, "and I was able to see clearly."

"So what do you make of that?" I asked.

"Obviously, it's about leaving you. I think I was myself as well as the optician. I know I look good on the outside, but the question is, 'Can I see clearly without you?' I think I can now."

Tears drifted down her cheeks.

"I think I'm going to be okay. But I want to know that I can come back if I need to."

I cleared my throat in an attempt to keep down a sob that was rising in my chest.

My impulse was to say, "I'll always be here if you need me." But then, I thought, I might not always be here. I might die like Joan. I remembered a conversation I had with a friend about what to say when a child is afraid of monsters under the bed. He had said to his daughter, "I'm going to kill those monsters under your bed. Bang, bang they're dead. Now you can go to sleep." But I was worried about lying.

I spoke softly as if I was reassuring a child that I would see her after nursery school. "I will always be here if you need me."

Once the words came out, the tears flowed—hers and mine. Mary Elizabeth's weeping was more intense, like moans, while mine were calmer. After a few minutes she quieted down and was able to speak.

"You've changed my life. I'm not the same person I was when I came here. Remember how afraid I was of loving you. I said, 'Don't make me love you.' I didn't understand what that meant then. I'm not afraid any more. I love you."

"I don't think you were just afraid of loving me. I think you were afraid of loving anyone," I said.

"Yes. I was afraid of hurting anyone I love as well as being hurt. Afraid of hurting them even more. Well, I guess that's my mother and father. I was afraid that I hurt her and I was incredibly hurt by him. I don't think I'm afraid any more. I don't feel lethal and I feel like I have the right glasses so I will be able to find someone to love."

She was looking at me intently as if to reassure me that she would be fine and I shouldn't worry about her. I imagined a little girl saying, "Don't worry Mom, I have my snack in my book bag and I'm set to go."

I was surprised and happy that Mary Elizabeth felt confident about meeting a man. And I thought she was right. She *did* look good; she didn't look like a parochial school girl any more. I could see the lace from her camisole peeking out of her blouse and her hair was stylishly cut. It no longer looked like she had just taken out the rollers.

"Okay, I'm ready."

She got up from the couch. She had stopped crying.

"I'd like to hug you and say goodbye."

I was taken aback.

"We have some time left," I said.

"I know, but I want to be the one to end the session."

"You want to feel in control?" I asked, knowing the answer.

"Yes. Is that okay? Can we do it that way?" she asked.

She wanted my permission. I smiled to reassure her.

"Sure. We can do it that way," I said.

"Can I hug you?" she asked timidly.

"Yes, of course."

I got up from my chair and she hugged me. I put my arms around her and she started to sob again. She could barely speak.

"I love you. Thank you for everything." She turned around and took one more admiring look at the Stargazers. Then she walked out the door.

The Eulogy

I sat on the Lexington Avenue subway reading the typed pages I had neatly folded in my purse. I had been writing and revising the eulogy ever since Joan stopped working. I did not imagine I was going to speak at Joan's funeral, but the act of writing the eulogy was a way of working through the reality of her impending death.

"Hi, Rose, it's Rachel," she had said, with her voice cracking.

I gasped, although I knew it was coming.

"My mother died last night," she was breathing deeply into the phone.

"Oh, Rachel," I sobbed, "I'm so sorry."

"I know … I know you really loved her. And she knew it too. So, I want you to speak about her at the funeral. Is that okay with you?"

"Oh, I can't tell you how much that would mean to me," I said.

"I know. I'll see you on Friday."

Now I was prepared for the task—my black Armani suit felt appropriate and the words felt right. Suddenly I looked up and realized I had taken the wrong train.

I ran off the train, sweating under the weight of my sheepskin coat, weaving my way through the onslaught of people to get to the Times Square shuttle. Frantic, I ran up the stairs cursing the annoying people who pushed their way down the left side of the steps, leaving no space for people going up. I ranted at whoever left an empty Coke can on the third step for someone to slip on. I debated whether to pick it up or risk the guilt of some old lady breaking her hip when she tumbled down the stairs. I couldn't live with the guilt so I picked it up.

A woman behind me was singing: "Jesus loves me no matter what I'm going through…" She said, "Young lady, do you think Jesus loves me?" I didn't know if I was the "young lady," but I didn't want to answer anyway. I was afraid if I gave her the bad news she might respond violently. At the top of the stairs, sweaty and out of breath, as I searched for a garbage pail to deposit the sticky can, I heard her singing:

> When your life's about to start—God is watching you,
> When you have a shattered heart—God is watching you,
> When you're a slave and when you're freed—God is watching you,
> When what you call love's really need—God is watching you.

I could not find a trash can, so I stood the can up next to a wall where no one would fall on it, and ran toward the shuttle. I barely made it onto the train; I put my sticky hand out to pry open the doors.

The shuttle was taking an eternity to get to Times Square. When it finally arrived, I pushed through the crowded and narrow passageway toward the uptown express. When I exited at 96th Street, it was a gloomy, cold February day, but beads of sweat rolled down my neck. I ran over to Amsterdam Avenue and headed south until I saw a large group of people milling around outside the Plaza Funeral Home at 91st Street.

It was familiar to me. I had been there for Sally's funeral six months earlier. Sitting in the last row, I had listened to her husband, brother and best friend give eulogies for her. They talked about her humor and warmth, her generosity and eloquence. I didn't know that Sally. The Sally I knew was struggling to cover up her vulnerability and terror. Did they know her better? Did I know her better? Just before she died she had begun to let me into rooms that had been locked up for decades. We had just started to open the windows and clear out the cob webs together. I had just begun to love her... A wave of depression washed over me. What was the point of the work we did together if she died before we were finished? I thought about the conversation about Camus I'd had with Dorothy. I remembered the phrase: "...in the end we die." It's true we all have separate life trajectories and in the end we die, but then I thought of Joan, and the wave receded. Along the way we have points of connection that are transformative.

Now, as I approached the funeral home, I overheard an argument that was going on about the psychoanalytic licensing bill, between Judy, Frank and Vicki—colleagues of Joan's from the Freudian Society whom I'd met when they visited her. Tim, Caroline and Jennifer, members of my peer supervision group, were hurrying to finish their coffee before going inside. There were a few loners as well. I wondered if the dark young woman standing off to the side with her handkerchief ready was one of Joan's patients. She came to cry, not to socialize. Leaning on a parked BMW was the blond "lawyer" I'd envied for so long. She was wearing a black suit and a silk blouse quite similar to mine. I realized that the short heavy woman looking like she'd been crying for days was the woman I used to call "the Lilliputian." I wondered if she was still seeing Joan when she stopped practicing.

I recognized Barbara, the receptionist from Washington Square Institute when I first started treatment with Joan. She seemed shorter than I remembered... But I was sure it was her. She glanced toward me, but didn't recognize me. A man with a yarmulke came out and invited us all to come inside. "Please take your seats in the main hall." Strange that it was a Jewish funeral, Joan was so un-Jewish. When I walked into the lobby, Rachel was welcoming people. I got on the end of the line, but she made eye contact with me, greeting me with a silent hug. Once I had wanted to be Joan's daughter, not Rachel particularly, but the person who could talk to her endlessly and didn't have to pay for the privilege. I glanced into the room where the service was going to take place. There was a large sign at the entrance: Joan Wiseman, February 1, 1973, 10 a.m."

Next to the podium on both sides were opulent arrangements of white calla lilies that Rachel had ordered. They were elegant in their simplicity and seemed so appropriate for the occasion. I read somewhere that the Romans planted them to bloom for winter solstice as if to bring the light indoors during the darkest days of the year. The white flowers emerged from stems that looked like giant celery stalks. I could understand why Georgia O'Keeffe was so taken by them. Someone told me she once said, "I'll paint it big so even busy New Yorkers take time to see what I see of flowers." But these flowers didn't need any magnification. They spired to three feet or more in their tall, clear glass vases and their snowy white spathes were two or three inches apart with yellow phallic centers.

When everyone had paid their respects to Rachel, they filed into the main room. Rachel and two of Joan's oldest and closest friends spoke, and then the rabbi turned toward me and asked me to come to the front to speak about Joan. They had all told warm and funny anecdotes about Joan—as a mother, colleague and friend. I was going to talk about Joan as a psychoanalyst.

I was standing in front of a large room filled with people who knew and loved Joan. Rachel, her father, and Joan's brother and his wife and children were sitting in the front row with Maria. Many of the people there were psychoanalysts and I knew a lot of them. Others were Joan's former patients. The Lilliputian held a fistful of tissues that she pressed to her puffy eyes. The rest were family and friends who I didn't know.

"I loved Joan." My voice started to crack immediately. "Frida Kahlo said about Diego Rivera, 'He took me shattered and returned me in one piece, whole.' I could say the same thing about Joan." I wiped my tears with a white cotton handkerchief. "I first went to see Joan when I was 21, and stayed in treatment with her for about four years." My eyes met the eyes of the "lawyer" in the third row whose black mascara left a trail down her cheek. "Indeed, I was one of her first patients." I smiled at her to indicate I knew she was one of the first as well.

"Some analyses feel like the analyst and patient are observing a pond or a lake together." The muscles in my neck and shoulders relaxed. I saw Anne sitting in the back smiling at me with her handkerchief at the ready. "There are frogs and tadpoles, water lilies floating on the surface with underwater stems rooted in the mud below. There are zooplankton and other varieties of algae and fish with different colors and textures. It's very calm on the surface, but underneath, when you analyze dreams and associations, there's passion, fighting, alcoholism, parents abandoning children, incest, or a whole bunch of other things."

"My analysis, on the other hand, was more like an ocean." I was heaving so intensely that I couldn't speak for a minute. "There were gigantic waves and a severe undertow. There were tiger sharks, lionfish, stingrays and poison jellyfish in the water. They weren't deep under the water, but close to the surface. No diving was necessary. We didn't have to analyze my dreams or follow my associations to observe my aggression. I yelled at her regularly. The attacks, stings and poisonous barbs emerged in the sessions repeatedly. I don't think there are many analysts who would have survived with me in those waters. But Joan was comfortable in that turbulent sea." The handkerchief I'd brought was a crumpled ball of tears and snot. "At one point I had been so enraged at her for such a protracted period that her unconscious overtook her and she went shopping instead of coming to my session with her." The therapists in the audience laughed and the patients were horrified, putting their hands over their mouths or grimacing in pain.

"We analyzed it and it was a turning point in the treatment. I always felt that whatever emerged in the treatment, we would analyze it and it would be okay—more grist for the mill as Joan always said." I mopped my cheeks again.

"Being a psychoanalyst differs from most other kinds of work; it is not simply a job in which you behave in a particular role or perform a variety of services. Rather, doing psychoanalysis involves using your *self*. And Joan's sense of self was unwavering. No matter what I threw at her, she rarely faltered in giving a calm transference interpretation.

"I accused her angrily, 'You don't love me.' But she was unflappable; she calmly tolerated my disappointment and anger—at least most of the time. She saw the yearning beneath. Joan always knew those feelings were about my mother and that she could not cure me simply by loving me. She understood all that pain had to come out if I was going to move beyond it. Love is not enough when it's remedial—she taught me that and it's served me well as an analyst. You can't be fully engaged in the present until you've slogged through the past. That's why allowing the transference to develop is so crucial in psychoanalytic work.

"While thinking about today," I continued, "which I have been doing for a couple of months, I went back to a book that Joan often referred to during my analysis, *The Little Prince*. At one point, the fox says to the little prince:

If you tame me, then we shall need each other.
To me, you shall be unique in the world.

To you, I shall be unique in the world.

"Well, Joan tamed me—literally and figuratively. And to me, she was unique in all the world."

When I left the podium and climbed down the few steps to where the mourners were seated, Rachel stood up and put her arms around me; she was smiling through her sobs.

"That was wonderful. I'm sure my mother loved it."

The rabbi came back to the podium to say a few words and then everyone got up to leave. Rachel took my hand and picked up one of the vases with white calla lilies. She handed it to me.

"I want you to have this," she said. "I think that next to me you loved my mother more than anyone in the world. She knew that and I'm sure that she'd want you to have them."

I put my arms around Rachel and held her tight. The tears on her cheeks mingled with mine. In a few moments her father and other friends and relatives started clamoring for her attention and I released my grip on her.

I picked up the vase and stared at the blooms for a few seconds. I had always wanted to be a calla lily, tall and elegant. But I spent most of my life acting like its closest relative, the skunk cabbage, which smells like a skunk when injured. Until I started seeing Joan, I had spent my life hoping that people would see through my camouflage and appreciate the inner scroll. She was the only person before Stephen who saw my inner calla lily. She understood that even when I was stuck being a skunk cabbage, my stink was an adaptation to the swamp I grew up in, and protected a vulnerable center.

Signs of Life

It was almost Memorial Day and I was pregnant. It had been over a year since I first visited Joan and four months since she had died. The daffodils and narcissus were turning brown in our meadow in Connecticut as the plants stored up their strength for next year. Since the rule of thumb is to delay planting annuals until the end of the May, I was now getting the garden ready for summer plantings. I watched a red wriggler make its way through the leaves, newspaper, coffee grinds, grass clipping and vegetable peels that I'd been composting throughout the spring. The tiny red worms were miraculous—they had consumed half their weight in organic matter each day and left behind a mound of rich fertilizer. There were a few leftover eggshells and tomato skins, but mostly the worms had done their work, spinning the leftovers into brown gold. It no longer smelled like the rotting material it had once been. Now its odor was earthy and fresh.

I shoveled the compost through an old screen to filter out the food waste that had not yet fully decomposed. It looked like crumbly chocolate cake as I pushed it through the holes in the screen.

The bladelike green shoots of the Asiatic lilies were already sprouting through the dirt —harbingers of the purples with white edges, deep saturated pinks, and white Stargazers I knew would be blooming soon. Carefully, I spooned the humus around each shoot and then shoveled the rich dirt onto the bed, where I was planting the calla lily and dahlia tubers.

I didn't mind the twinge in my lower back that came from bending over, or the growing soreness in my right forearm from shoveling. The pain was testimony to my contribution to what was a natural process. I stopped and closed my eyes, feeling the sun on my face, swatting the mayflies that buzzed around my neck and ears. Then I poured the compost on the soil I had loosened for planting the annuals—white forget-me-nots, purple lisianthus, red salvia, and purple verbena. A fat earthworm worked its way up to the surface—the pointy end poking up first. Its segmented body constricted to propel it across the earth in waves. Scooping it up with the crumbly soil, I spread it on the perennial bed—feeding the delphiniums, monarda and columbines that showed no signs of life as of yet. But I knew they would be coming back.

Acknowledgements

I could not have written this book without my husband Richard Wool, who edited and offered insightful comments on the multiple drafts over the many years it took to complete. Victoria Mills encouraged me to keep going during periods of self-doubt. Phyllis Stern was a dedicated copy editor and proofreader. Most of all, I would not be the person I am without my analyst, the late Joan Klein.

About the Author

Roberta Satow, Ph.D. is a practicing psychoanalyst in Washington, CT. She is a senior member of the faculty and control analyst at the National Psychological Association for Psychoanalysis. She is Professor Emerita of Sociology at Brooklyn College and the Graduate Center of the City University of New York. In addition to her non-fiction book *Doing the Right Thing: Taking Care of Your Elderly Parents Even if They Didn't Take Care of You* (Tarcher/Penguin 2006), she has written a novel *Two Sisters of Coyoacan* (2017) and edited *Gender and Social Life* (Allyn and Bacon, 2000).

Printed in the USA
CPSIA information can be obtained
at www.ICGtesting.com
LVHW021917020424
775860LV00005B/46